Maximizing Your Marriage

A Marriage Enrichment Course For Couples

STUDENT WORKBOOK

Name: _____

Dr. Daryl G. Donovan

CSS Publishing Company, Inc., Lima, Ohio

MAXIMIZING YOUR MARRIAGE
STUDENT WORKBOOK

For more information about CSS Publishing Company resources, visit our website at
www.csspub.com or e-mail us at custserv@csspub.com or call (800) 241-4056.

ISBN 0-7880-2337-3

PRINTED IN U.S.A.

***Maximizing Your Marriage** is dedicated to all of those couples
who seek to have strong, vibrant marriages
that reflect the person and character of Christ.*

*And to
my wife Elaine, my helper and best friend,
and my children, Rebekah, Kristen, Benjamin, and Kay,
my greatest joy in life who have taught me more about
marriage and family than any book could.*

*And to
Pete and Sandra Kyne, whose marriage reflects Jesus,
and who have labored alongside me
to see this project become a reality.*

Table Of Contents

Preface

God intends for marriage to be the most satisfying life-giving human relationship you will experience on this planet. The marital union is to be a type, picture, or reflection of the union between Christ and his church (Ephesians 5:32). We are the bride of Christ. Our relationship with our spouse should be like our relationship with Christ: a source of joy, peace, life, and love. Many marriages miss God's plan. Nearly fifty percent fail, resulting in divorce. Many who remain married experience constant turmoil and strife.

Maximizing Your Marriage is a tool to help get couples headed in the right direction to experience and enjoy all God wants for them.

Instructions To Students

This workbook is intended to be used by an individual. Each person will do his/her assignments alone, at home, without discussion prior to the small group sessions. Complete the assignments carefully and honestly prior to coming to class.

For Sessions 1-9, a list will be passed for you to sign up to bring in a snack for all to share. It is not necessary to bring in a fancy snack, just something for the break period.

The last session is designed as a getaway weekend, so begin planning now to enjoy a weekend with each other. The details will be given to you soon.

Do not be tempted to work ahead in your workbooks, and be respectful of your spouse's workbook (answers). Do not compare notes prior to class. Although sharing responses in class is not mandatory, it will be more beneficial if you share from time to time. Use the blank page at the end of each session for taking notes.

Weekly Schedule For Sessions 1-9
   Greeting and Prayer
   Roll Call
   Game
   Overview of Session
   Break period (snacks)
   Small group time
   Gather for closing at a set time

Some Tips To Keep
Your Marriage In Jesus' Hands

Pray daily for your spouse/children.

Have a regular quiet-time of prayer and Bible reading.

Pray regularly out loud, holding hands with your spouse.

Participate in a vibrant, Christ-centered church.

Have someone who can help you be accountable in your Christian walk.

Be quick to admit sin, be willing to repent, and be ready to forgive and receive forgiveness.

Ask often to be filled and empowered with the Holy Spirit.

Confidential
Marriage Questionnaire

Name: _____   Date of Birth: _____

Date of Marriage: _____   Years Married: _____

How long did you know each other prior to marriage? _____

Did you receive pre-marital counseling prior to marriage? _____
Describe: _____
_____
_____
_____

What would you consider to be the greatest strengths of your marriage?
_____
_____
_____
_____

What do you consider to be the greatest weaknesses of your marriage?
_____
_____
_____
_____

What specific problem areas do you face currently as a couple?
(Can be similar to response above, but be more specific.)
_____
_____
_____
_____

What do you hope to see happen as a result of this course?
_____
_____
_____
_____

Have you been involved in a previous marriage? _____
If yes, briefly tell the cause of the failure of that union: _____
_____
_____
_____
_____

Rate the following aspects of your marriage
(1 to 10 with 10 being best)

Communication

    0   1   2   3   4   5   6   7   8   9   10

Comment: _____

Unity

    0   1   2   3   4   5   6   7   8   9   10

Comment: _____

Mutual Respect

    0   1   2   3   4   5   6   7   8   9   10

Comment: _____

Commitment

    0   1   2   3   4   5   6   7   8   9   10

Comment: _____

Financial Stability and Peace

    0   1   2   3   4   5   6   7   8   9   10

Comment: _____

Intimacy (closeness, may relate to sexual relationship)

    0   1   2   3   4   5   6   7   8   9   10

Comment: _____

Mutual Understanding

    0   1   2   3   4   5   6   7   8   9   10

Comment: _____

Christ-Centeredness

    0   1   2   3   4   5   6   7   8   9   10

Comment: _____

Mutual Submission To Christ

... always giving thanks for all things in the name of our Lord Jesus Christ to God, even the Father, and be subject to one another in the fear of Christ.
                                                          — Ephesians 5:20-21

Briefly write your own personal testimony of how and when you came to know Christ as your Savior. Share a sentence or two about what your relationship with Jesus means to you right now.

_____

_____

_____

_____

_____

_____

_____

_____

_____

_____

Christ The Solid Rock

Why would a study about marriage begin with a couple sharing their personal testimonies about how they came to Christ? The reason is that your marriage can never be all God intends for it to be without Jesus Christ at the very center. He is the sure foundation of a happy home.

Jesus told a parable that illustrates how essential it is that our heart and our home be established in him.

"Therefore everyone who hears these words of Mine and acts on them, may be compared to a wise man who built his house on the rock. And the rain fell, and the floods came, and the winds blew and slammed against that house; and yet it did not fall, for it had been founded on the rock. Everyone who hears these words of Mine and does not act on them, will be like a foolish man who built his house on the sand. The rain fell, and the floods came, and the winds blew and slammed against that house; and it fell — and great was its fall."
                                                          — Matthew 7:24-27

On a scale of 1 to 10 (10 being most), to what degree are you confident that your marriage is being built securely on Jesus, the Solid Rock?

| 0 | 1 | 2 | 3 | 4 | 5 | 6 | 7 | 8 | 9 | 10 |

Explain: _____

_____

_____

For the two of you to experience the joy of oneness in your marriage, each of you must know Jesus personally as Savior and Lord. Please understand that knowing *about* Jesus and knowing Jesus are not the same thing. Being a Christian is not a mere mental consent of saying, "Oh sure, I believe in Jesus. I believe He came to earth, died on the cross and rose from the dead." Even the demons believe and know all of that (James 2:19).

Being a Christian is not only believing in Jesus; it is receiving Jesus. In that receiving of Jesus, there is the surrender of one's life to the rule and reign of Christ. Jesus said, "If you love Me, you will obey Me" (John 14:23). It is a life, as the Apostle Paul wrote where "it is no longer I who live, but Christ lives in me, and the life which I now live in the flesh I live by faith in the Son of God, who loved me, and delivered Himself up for me" (Galatians 2:20).

When two people who belong to Jesus, who have Christ living in them are united as one, something very precious and powerful happens. A union is established that is destined to grow and prosper. Paul, in his brief message about marriage, begins with a strong exhortation: "Be subject to one another in the fear (or in reverence) of Christ" (Ephesians 5:21). He is saying that a couple must be diligent to keep Christ as the head and centerpiece of their lives.

What Difference Does Jesus Make?
Several things are unique about a relationship that is firmly established in Jesus. Even the non-Christian population has been forced to acknowledge that there is something different about Christian marriages. More than one secular poll revealed statistical results demonstrating that Christian couples remain married three to one over non-Christians. Jesus does make a difference.

Distinction #1: Givers Not Takers
One of the clearest differences with Christian marriages is how the couple relate to each other. You see, a Christian is one who has been made complete in Christ. The word *salvation* has at its root meaning the concept of wholeness. In Christ, there is joy, peace, purpose, acceptance, forgiveness, love, and more. A Christian has found fulfillment in Christ.

In a Christian marriage neither is looking to the other to be fulfilled. Having been fulfilled, made complete, whole and significant, each comes into the relationship equipped to give — not striving to get. Simply put, Christians are givers not takers.

Once a young woman came to me desperate to be married. She said she was so lonely. She feared being an old maid. I told her not to get married to fill that need of loneliness. She needed to get close to the One (Jesus Christ) who would meet that need first, then look for a man to marry. She ignored that counsel, married an over-the-road truck driver, and now is despairing in depression.

In your marriage, rate yourself as to what degree you are a giver or a taker (10 is the biggest giver).

0	1	2	3	4	5	6	7	8	9	10

Explain: _____

_____

Distinction #2: Serving As Christ Served

Paul wrote: "Whatever you do in word or deed, do all in the name of the Lord Jesus Christ, giving thanks through him to God the Father" (Colossians 3:17). Speaking or doing in Jesus' name literally means to do it as his representative — or perhaps better said, to do it as Christ would. Yes, it's a little like the popular slogan seen on wristbands and bumper stickers: WWJD. What would Jesus do?

Because Christ is in us, Christians are to be those who reflect the character, words, and actions of our Lord. The way this is lived out in a marriage is that both the husband and wife intentionally (and joyfully) treat one another as Jesus would. Would Jesus ever demean another with harsh or cruel words? Would Jesus deceive or be unfaithful? Setting our hearts, with the empowerment of the Holy Spirit, to love and serve one another as Christ did, will foster a life-giving relationship in your marriage. Although there will be times we will stumble and fail to reflect Christ, as we press on to allow him to develop his character in us, we will continue to grow in Christ-likeness. As a couple who belong to him, he will enable you to fulfill the charge to speak and act as his representatives.

List ways you can serve your spouse as Christ would:
1. _____
2. _____
3. _____

Distinction #3: As Unto The Lord

Paul did not merely challenge Christians to do what they do as Jesus would. He went a step further. In Colossians 3:23 he wrote, "Whatever you do, do your work heartily, as for the Lord rather than for men." Paul is saying that we are to do what we do as we would unto Jesus.

Someone asked Mother Teresa how she could so willingly, lovingly, and tirelessly serve people who were ungrateful, unloving and enemies of her Christ. She replied that she looked into their eyes and saw the eyes of Jesus and served them as she would serve him.

So you see, Christians are not only to serve as Jesus served, but we are to serve one another as if we were serving Jesus. Christian couples see Jesus in one another and so when they speak or act, they do so as if speaking to Jesus — or as doing something for Jesus. Would we speak harshly to Jesus? Would we selfishly or thoughtlessly put off a request that he had made of us? Wouldn't we seek to bless our Lord, to honor him, and to take advantage of every opportunity to demonstrate our love for him?

What does it mean to you to treat your spouse as you would treat Jesus? _____
_____
_____

To what degree have you been effective at interacting with your spouse as you would unto Jesus? (10 is best)

0	1	2	3	4	5	6	7	8	9	10

Explain: _____
_____
_____

Distinction #4: On A Fast Track Forward

Before you beat yourself up about distinctions 1, 2, and 3, feeling you have failed as a godly mate, let me encourage you that Christ is at work in you — and he will complete the work he began.

Someone once said, "It is not so much where a person is as where he or she is headed." We will fail — but we will press on, "fixing our eyes on Jesus" (Hebrews 12:2).

One of the greatest distinctions of all for Christian couples is that Christ is the common bond as well as the common pursuit. As Paul wrote to the Christians at Rome, "We are being conformed to the image of God's Son" (Romans 8:29). We are in process. (Men prefer to say we are "under construction.")

When a man and a woman have set their sights to be closer to Jesus, more like Jesus, fully submitted to Jesus, their marriage will only grow richer and sweeter as the years go by. You will find that as you draw closer to him, you will draw closer to one another. Fix your eyes on him.

List some things you can do as a couple to draw closer to the Lord, and thereby draw closer to one another.
1. _____
2. _____
3. _____
4. _____
5. _____

Have there been recent hurts you have caused your spouse by not reflecting the character, words, or actions of Jesus? ___ yes ___ no

Explain: _____

_____

_____

Distinction #5: Empowered With The Holy Spirit

A couple of verses back from where Paul told us to "be subject to one another in the fear of Christ," he wrote, "... be filled with the Holy Spirit." In the original Greek text those words are in the present active tense which means Paul is saying "... keep on being filled with the Holy Spirit." There is a daily need for the filling, indwelling power of the Holy Spirit for us to experience abundant life and vibrant marriages.

In Galatians 5:22-23, Paul lists the fruit of the Holy Spirit: "But the fruit of the Spirit is love, joy, peace, patience, kindness, goodness, faithfulness, gentleness, self-control; against such things there is no law." By calling these character qualities "fruit" there is the very clear proclamation that they are a result of the Holy Spirit working in us, not a work of our flesh striving to produce them. Only surrendering to the work and will of the Spirit of God in your life will produce this kind of good fruit.

Christian couples have the remarkable distinction of the empowerment of the Holy Spirit producing good fruit. While others strain to love each other rightly, or to find peace or joy — or to be patient, the Christian couple experiences the Holy Spirit developing these qualities in them as they are being transformed. Simply said, Christian couples have the "helper," the Holy Spirit working in them producing good fruit.

Circle the fruit listed below that you desire to have the Holy Spirit enlarge or increase in you.

Love	Joy	Peace	Patience	Kindness	Goodness

Faithfulness   Gentleness   Self-Control

Explain: _____

_____

_____

Time With The Master Marriage Builder

Take time to ask forgiveness of one another for failures of reflecting Christ. Join hands as you pray, giving thanks to God for your spouse — and for the assurance that Jesus is at work in your marriage.

Notes

The Wonder Of God's Oneness

Some Pharisees came to him, testing Him and asking, "Is it lawful for a man to divorce his wife for any reason at all?" And he answered and said, "Have you not read that He who created them from the beginning MADE THEM MALE AND FEMALE and said, "FOR THIS REASON A MAN SHALL LEAVE HIS FATHER AND MOTHER AND BE JOINED TO HIS WIFE, AND THE TWO SHALL BECOME ONE FLESH?" So they are no longer two, but one flesh. What therefore God has joined together, let no man separate.

— Matthew 19:3-6

God loves marriage. Marriage is meant to be the most fulfilling, life-giving, earthly relationship we will experience. It is a sad commentary on our culture that marriage has fallen into such dismal decay. Nearly fifty percent of marriages end in divorce, and about half of the fifty percent who stay together are miserable. Why do we see such a marital mess?

We must remember there is an adversary seeking to devour — to steal and destroy anything good God creates. The devil is not brilliant (he was foolish enough to rebel against God), but he is smart enough to know he cannot touch God. He knows God is more powerful. So what the devil does rather than going after God is to attack those things God loves most.

For centuries Satan has led an active, destructive campaign against the institution of marriage and family. Because God loves marriage so much, the enemy presses hard to destroy that which is dear to the Father's heart.

Why does God love marriage so much? The Apostle Paul gives us insight to this question when we read his commentary on marriage in Ephesians 5. He wrote, "For this cause a man shall leave his father and mother, and shall cleave to his wife; and the two shall become one flesh. This mystery is great; but I am speaking with reference to Christ and the church" (Ephesians 5:31-32).

God loves marriage because it is a picture of the covenantal relationship he has with us. At the conclusion of Paul's words about marriage, he tells us that what he is *really* talking about is the union between Christ and his church. Remember, we are the Bride of Christ. He is the Bridegroom. The imagery of oneness, intimacy, and an unbreakable covenant between a man and a woman are equally true of what God desires for each of his own. In other words, when the world peeks in and observes our marriage, they ought to catch a glimpse of what God wants us all to experience with him.

The devil understands the picture the Father wants the world to see in our marriage — so he passionately pursues to cloud and even mar that image.

17

You see there is far more at stake in the success or failure of your marriage than your mere happiness. The character and purposes of God are on the line. The greatest opportunity to testify of the love and life-giving nature of the Father is present in your union. For this reason we must guard and nurture the oneness of our marriage. As we allow the Spirit of God to work in our hearts and home, the world will see the love and power of Christ. It is time for Christians to stand firm, to take up the whole armor of God, to resist the devil and his schemes, and in the strength of God's might to experience marital oneness that brings delight to ourselves and to the Father.

List some things the enemy has done to attack your marriage.

_____
_____
_____

How did you respond? _____

_____
_____

Guarding And Nurturing Oneness
Describe what marital oneness means to you.

_____
_____
_____
_____
_____
_____

In a marital union God brings two unique, precious individuals together and mysteriously transforms them for all time. Even though you remain unique as an individual, the mystical merger now enriches your own uniqueness with another human soul. You soon discover that the words "I," "me," and "mine" fade into sweet words of "we," "us," and "ours." Your thoughts become filled with new desires of a common bond. You experience the expression of desires or emotions without words. A life-long process is underway of God fostering a oneness that will enhance your lives and enlarge your witness to the world.

Because this oneness is so precious to God, and so vital for you, intentionally guard it and nurture it. In every aspect of your life pursue unity and oneness in your marriage.

1. Spiritual Oneness
The Bible forbids the union of a believer to an unbeliever. "Do not be bound together with unbelievers; for what partnerships have righteousness and lawlessness, or what fellowship has light with darkness?" (2 Corinthians 6:14). If, in a marriage, one is a believer and the other is not, the two do not submit to the same master. In fact, they represent and dwell in two separate kingdoms. The believer submits to Jesus and walks in the kingdom of light, while the unbeliever submits to the

devil (or his or her own flesh), living in the kingdom of darkness. Spiritual disharmony of this nature will lead to constant conflict, strife, and dissatisfaction. God's love wants so much more for us.

Are you a committed Christian with a personal relationship with Jesus Christ?
         ___ yes   ___ no   ___ **I'm not sure**

Explain: _____
_____

Even though both may be Christians in a marriage, there may be serious spiritual disunity. While the couple need not think exactly alike on every spiritual issue of life, areas that create conflict must be given attention.

> *Several years ago when I was teaching a finance class, a young woman asked a question about tithing. She informed me her husband didn't believe in tithing, but she did. Being a woman working out of the home she asked, "Is it okay if I tithe on my money?" I told her that she and her husband had a far deeper issue than tithing. The very fiber of the oneness of their marriage was in jeopardy.*

Over the years I've seen couples who miss the delight of spiritual oneness. There are those who have simply agreed to disagree on significant issues and have stopped talking about them. Some decide that he will have his church and she will have hers.

Tell about any areas of spiritual disunity in your marriage. _____
_____
_____
_____
_____
_____

Many of these spiritual differences can be resolved. Here are a few suggestions:
- Earnestly pray and ask God to bring you into unity. It is amazing how the God of all truth can reveal his heart and change our heart and our mind.
- Diligently study the topic of disagreement together, seeking to understand each other's position.
- Seek the counsel of your pastor or other trusted Christian mentor.
- Be willing to submit to the truth of the Bible over your own tradition or opinion.
- Wives, be willing to submit to your husband even if you still feel he is wrong (1 Peter 3:1-2). (This would *not* include participation in something illegal or immoral.)
- Be actively involved *together* in Christian opportunities or events. Don't overdo with "his stuff" or "her stuff."
- Daily join hands and briefly pray for one another, thanking God for your spouse.

Can you think of other steps to insure spiritual unity in your marriage?

_____

_____

2. Physical Oneness

We will spend an entire session dealing with the physical aspect of your relationship, specifically dealing with the area of sexual intercourse. God has given the gift of sex to a couple to experience a physical oneness that is intimate and unexplainably powerful.

In 1 Corinthians 7:4, Paul makes a profound statement about the physical union between a man and woman. "The wife does not have authority over her own body, but the husband does; and likewise also the husband does not have authority over his own body, but the wife does."

What does 1 Corinthians 7:4 mean to you? _____

_____

_____

_____

_____

_____

_____

The overarching principle of scripture when it comes to physical oneness is one of mutual consent. 1 Corinthians 7:5 says to "Stop depriving one another, except by *agreement* for a time that you may devote yourselves to prayer, and come together again lest Satan tempt you because of your lack of self-control."

If a man and a woman understand that their bodies are no longer their own, that they have willingly relinquished authority over their own bodies, then the principle of mutual agreement must be the result. In other words, sexual intercourse is a mutual decision whether to engage in it or refrain from it. The husband does not say to the wife, "We will have sex tonight whether you like it or not." The wife does not say to the husband, "Because you forgot my birthday there will be no sex tonight."

The biblical design for physical oneness is that the decision about sexual intercourse is always mutual. Often that mutuality is found through sensitivity and candid conversation. Much of the time the husband and wife are at a very different place when it comes to sexual interest and desire which requires loving dialogue to move them toward mutual unity.

List some situations where mutual consent to refrain from sexual intercourse would be appropriate.

_____

_____

_____

_____

_____

Mutual consent is not always easy to obtain, but it is always best. The commitment to strive for mutuality will guard the oneness, as well as the ecstasy of your sexual relationship.

3. Philosophical Oneness

Two individuals bring their own set of philosophical understandings into a relationship. A person's "philosophy" about life is his or her system of values or attitudes about existence. For example, one philosophy about the environment is that we are to protect it with extreme measures. A contrary philosophy would say that it's all here for us to plunder. There are philosophies in between those two extremes. Some people are philosophically conservative, while others are moderate or liberal.

Take a moment to complete this philosophical survey.

Philosophical Check List
Circle the answer closest to your opinion.

1. Politically I am: Liberal   Conservative   Moderate

2. When it comes to spending I am: Frugal   Carefree   Balanced

3. My idea of a good time is: Staying Home   Going Dancing   Going Out To A Movie

4. When a child disobeys, it's time to: Talk   Spank   Ignore

5. If we can't have children: We Won't   We'll Adopt   We'll Implant

6. When it comes to children, we'll have: None   One   Two   Three Or More

7. The house shall be led: By the Husband   Equally Both   Whoever Is Strongest

8. Our children will be educated in: Public School   Private School   Home School

9. Abortion is: Wrong   A Woman's Right   An Okay Alternative

10. Homosexuality is: A Sin   An Acceptable Alternative   None Of My Business

When you review this session with your spouse, list any significant philosophical differences.

_____

_____

_____

The two of you were not meant to think exactly alike, however the Bible speaks to the issue of philosophical differences: "How can two walk together unless they have agreement?" (Amos 3:3).

If you have serious philosophical differences that have put your oneness at risk, you may want to seek counsel. You may discover you are in greater agreement than you thought, or that the issue was not as significant to you as you once thought.

When Elaine and I began to have children, I started thinking about their future education. I was excited about the thought of all the activities and events (sports, band, and such) public school provides. Then we met a precious family that homeschooled their children. I could tell that Elaine was impressed with their success. I was adamant in my philosophical value that children need the opportunities and the socialization of public school. We were at opposite poles of the philosophical spectrum. Together, we launched into study and prayer, with many "stimulating" conversations. Because we are committed to unity in our marriage, we worked hard to find a place of commonality and peace — and we did.

Tell about a philosophical issue that once divided you but has now been resolved. Tell how you found resolution.

_____
_____
_____
_____
_____
_____

4. Practical Oneness

You share a common name as husband and wife. Share all other things in common as well (other than inappropriate items like underwear, razors, or toothbrushes). Right after our wedding I sold my car and Elaine sold her car. Together we bought "our" car. That may not seem too significant, but something deeper than a car title happened in our relationship. Practical oneness enhances all other aspects of oneness, and in fact is a visible manifestation of that oneness.

Look for every opportunity to transform the words "mine" into "ours." As much as possible share common activities, yet graciously allow freedom for individual expression. Have joint titles of ownership, joint accounts, as well as common responsibility for all major purchases. Guard the unity of your marriage by seeking practical oneness at every turn.

On a scale of 1-10, 1 being more individual and 10 being total oneness, rate your marriage as to practical oneness.

     0   1   2   3   4   5   6   7   8   9   10

List areas you have retained individual or separate ownership and tell why:

_____
_____
_____
_____

Practical oneness also relates to the relatives in your life. I've seen many marriages crippled by the fact that parents are permitted to have inappropriate influence on the oneness of their children's married life. The scripture says *leave* your father and mother.

God has established you as one, a family unit, responsible to be all God wants for you. While it may be necessary to seek the counsel of your parents occasionally, you must make your way to establish your own process of decision-making as a couple. Avoid depending upon your parents financially. There are times their assistance may be needed, but do not become dependent upon them. You are no longer their dependents.

When your parents come to visit, they need to knock before they enter your home, just as you do when you go to their home. Their home is no longer your home. What used to be your bedroom at their house is not your bedroom anymore. Their refrigerator is no longer open game for you. You are two individual households.

Is (or has) parental influence been a problem for you in your marriage?

___ yes   ___ no   ___ some

Explain: _____

_____

_____

An excellent resource to help you establish healthy boundaries with your extended family is the book, Boundaries *by Henry Cloud and John Townsend.*

Are there any areas in your marriage where you have deep concerns about your oneness?

___ Spiritual   ___ Physical   ___ Philosophical   ___ Practical

Discuss your response: _____

_____

_____

_____

_____

5. The Fruit Of Oneness
Oneness has great rewards. If you experience the kind of unity in your marriage God intends, you will enjoy some divine results.

1. There will be agreements on priorities. When in the setting of goals and priorities there is oneness, there is peace.

2. There will be perseverance for the hard times. Marriages go through storms, but where there is common faith and values, the couple will sustain those storms together.

3. There will be pleasure. Where there is unity, there is delight. While there will be conflicts, having common ground from which to work leads to healthy resolution.

4. There will be a faithful witness to the purposes and power of God. The lost will see what God can do in the lives of two people committed to Christ, and his love will be reflected.

23

Notes

A Promise To Be Kept

Some Pharisees came up to Jesus, testing Him, and began to question Him whether it was lawful for a man to divorce a wife. And he answered and said to them, "What did Moses command you?"

They said, "Moses permitted a man TO WRITE A CERTIFICATE OF DIVORCE AND SEND her AWAY." But Jesus said to them, "Because of your hardness of heart he wrote you this commandment. But from the beginning of creation, God MADE THEM MALE AND FEMALE. FOR THIS REASON A MAN SHALL LEAVE HIS FATHER AND MOTHER, AND THE TWO SHALL BECOME ONE FLESH; so they are no longer two, but one flesh. What therefore God has joined together, let no man separate."

In the house the disciples began questioning Him about this again. And He said to them, "Whosoever divorces his wife and marries another woman commits adultery against her; and if she herself divorces her husband and marries another man, she is committing adultery." — Mark 10:2-12

Jesus had a way about him that he always brought the focus in on the truth and the positive. When the Pharisees questioned him about divorce, Jesus turned the spotlight to marriage. The Pharisees didn't understand the heart of God concerning marriage. Marriage wasn't something decided or established by men — it was a "God-thing." "What God has joined together let no man separate." Who are we to think that we can simply rip apart the fabric of a relationship God has sewn together?

Marriage is a commitment. It is a lifelong promise. That promise begins with God. He promised to make you one — and he promised to provide for you all the resources you need to succeed. If a marriage fails, it is not because God has not faithfully kept his promise.

What do you think Jesus meant when he said, "What God has joined together, let no man separate"? _____
_____
_____
_____
_____

Vows For Life
On your wedding day you made vows (or promises) to one another before God — and usually before a gathering of people who love you. You promised that until death separated you, you would remain faithful to love and to honor one another. You said in sickness, poverty, or even worse, you would remain faithful to your pledge. The marriage vow is a serious commitment broken far too often.

Hank and Louise (the names are changed to protect their identity) decided to get married. They were ecstatic as were their eight stepchildren-to-be. You see Hank had been married twice with four children and Louise had been married three times with four children. As they met with the pastor to begin the process of preparing for the big day, the pastor asked a few probing questions. He asked Louise why her previous three marriages had failed. She replied, "Incompatibility! We just couldn't get along so I divorced them!" "How about you, Hank? What about your marriages?" Hank hung his head and murmured, "I was unfaithful to both of them."

The pastor with gracious boldness said, "So here we sit with both of you having broken promises. What would make you think you might keep the promises this time?" The two sat for a long few moments in silence until Louise spoke up and said, "Well, I guess we're at least willing to give it a try."

One of the reasons for the high degree of failure in marriage is the low degree of commitment on the part of the couple. Divorce has been made commonplace. Vows are not promises. They have become mere words.

To what degree are you resolved in your heart that your marriage vows are for life? (10 is best)

0	1	2	3	4	5	6	7	8	9	10

Explain: _____
_____
_____
_____
_____

How Worse Is Worse?

I performed a wedding once where the bride got tongue-tied. Instead of saying "for better or for worse," she said "for worse or for worse." I've always thought she probably knew the guy better than I did.

The question is: How worse is worse? When has a marriage gone so sour it can't be saved? Honestly, according to Jesus, and to the vows we make, there is never a total loss of hope. If you listen carefully, however, you hear a murmuring from the masses that there are a lot of good reasons to terminate a marriage.

Incompatibility, abuse, unfaithfulness, mental cruelty, deceit, love loss, I've heard all those reasons for divorce and more.

Ron came back from the war shell-shocked. He was totally, mentally incompetent. He had to be placed in a mental institution. Mary was encouraged to divorce him. Her friends told her she deserved a life, and that Ron could never be a real husband for her. She replied, "I promised in sickness or in health that I would never leave him." What rare devotion!

Jesus does give the possibility that unfaithfulness, or unchastity, is a reason for divorce. He makes it clear, however, that the real cause for marital failure is hardness of heart. One, or both, have made the decision that the marriage is over. The heart is hardened and set. Adultery is simply a symptom of hardness of heart. The inability to forgive and see a marriage restored is a hardness of heart issue. What destroys a marriage is a heart that has become calloused to God, unwilling to allow him to renew the marriage unto restoration.

There are no real grounds for divorce — there is only the hardness of a dirty heart that has destroyed the union. A *ground* implies a "right" to divorce, when at best God has given permission only.

Respond to the statement, "There are no grounds for divorce."

_____
_____
_____
_____

Commitment Is A Decision

The commitment to stay together is not a promise based on emotion or circumstances. It is a decision of the will that says "through thick and thin, warm feelings or cold, I will remain faithful to the vow until death."

> *Bill and Mary were so very much infatuated with each other. (They would say "in love.") As they met with the pastor they could hardly keep their hands off each other. As they discussed their wedding ceremony there were several changes they wanted made to make their service more contemporary. Mary made it very clear she did not want the words* obey *nor* submit *in the service. Bill said, "We don't want that Ephesians passage read. It's so old fashioned." When they came to the vows, Bill spoke up and said, "And, we don't want those words about staying together until death in there. We want you to say 'as long as we both shall love.' " After a trip to the restroom to relieve his nausea, the pastor informed the couple they needed to find someone else to perform their wedding.*

Emotions run hot and cold. The one you may feel passionate emotions of love for today may be the same one you feel intense anger and disdain for the next. You cannot base a marital commitment on emotion.

Have there been times that "emotionally" you were ready to "check out" of this marriage?

_____ **yes**   _____ **no**   _____ **somewhat**

Explain: _____
_____
_____

What did you do with those feelings? _____

_____

_____

Circumstances cannot be the basis for a successful marriage. As you will see in the session on finances, over ninety percent of couples who divorce say financial stress was the most significant factor in their failure. The money wasn't the issue. The vow was the factor. Remember the one about, "for richer or for poorer"?

I knew one couple in which after fifteen years of marriage the husband left because his wife had a double mastectomy. I sat with a weeping man whose wife packed up and left when they discovered he was sterile. Circumstances changed and suddenly the vow, "in sickness and in health" was only half true.

Tell about a circumstance that really tested your marriage and how you made it through.

_____

_____

_____

_____

_____

_____

Not A Vow To Tolerate
Couples are to be commended who have hung in there even when things have been tough in their marriage. They have been extremely tolerant and faithful to keep the lifelong pledge. While it is good and right that they have remained together, the vow is not one to merely tolerate each other until someone dies. The vow is to love and to cherish.

Just as commitment is a decision of the human will, so is love. Love is not just an emotion. You choose to love and cherish even when your feelings are somewhere else. Time and time again in scripture we are commanded to love. The very fact it is a command to love makes it clear that it is a willful decision.

True biblical love is a selfless sacrificial act expecting nothing in return. It is not conditionally based on right actions and responses. It finds its inception in the heart of the "lover" freely given to others. "God demonstrated His love for us in that while we were yet sinners, Christ died for us" (Romans 5:8). "God so loved the world that he gave his only begotten Son" (John 3:16). God's love certainly was not based upon our good behavior or correct responses. He "willed" to love us in spite of ourselves.

Both husband and wife are challenged to love and cherish, as Christ loved us. Not based on good behavior or correct responses, we promise to love and cherish for better *or worse* until death separates us.

28

Comment on this statement: "Love is not an emotion. It is an act of the will."

_____

_____

_____

_____

_____

_____

What About Temporary Separation?

It is clear that divorce is never God's best for us. He hates divorce (Malachi 2:16). Are there times when temporary separation can be a road to restoration for a marriage?

When extreme emotional or any physical abuse is taking place, separation is a valid option for any future reconciliation between the couple. When a marriage has reached this level of frustration, the couple is too emotionally "raw" to deal rightly with the issues at hand. In such circumstances, there may need to be a season of individual counseling before either is prepared for joint counseling.

If there is ongoing sexual infidelity, it may be fully appropriate to have the unfaithful spouse move out until there is repentance. Jesus did give permission for divorce under these circumstances, but let me encourage you to diligently pray and be certain divorce is your only option left.

Married Again, Already

Perhaps you're taking this course and you've already been through the painful process of divorce. You now are seeking to build a firm biblical foundation with a new spouse. Take time to prayerfully evaluate the failure of your first marriage and resolve in your heart things will be very different this time. Be sure you have confessed any sin or failings on your part so that you might fully experience God's cleansing forgiveness (1 John 1:9). Search your heart to be certain there is no unforgiveness that yet lingers from the previous marriage.

Notes

Expectations vs. Godly Assignments

Wives, be subject to your own husbands, as to the Lord. For the husband is the head of the wife, as Christ also is the head of the church. He Himself being the Savior of the body. But as the church is subject to Christ, so also the wives ought to be to their husbands in everything. Husbands, love your wives, just as Christ also loved the church and gave Himself up for her, so that He might sanctify her, having cleansed her by the washing to water with the word, that He might present to Himself the church in all her glory, having no spot or wrinkle or any such thing; but that she should be holy and blameless. So husbands ought also to love their own wives as their own bodies. He who loves his own wife loves himself; for no one ever hated his own flesh, but nourishes and cherishes it, just as Christ also does the church, because we are members of His body. FOR THIS REASON A MAN SHALL LEAVE HIS FATHER AND MOTHER AND SHALL BE JOINED TO HIS WIFE, AND THE TWO SHALL BECOME ONE FLESH. This mystery is great; but I am speaking with reference to Christ and the church. Nevertheless, each individual among you also is to love his own wife even as himself; and the wife must see to it that she respect her husband. — Ephesians 5:22-33

It is very clear in scripture that the Father has some clear assignments for both the husband and the wife in the union of marriage. Faithfully seeking to fulfill those God-given assignments or roles will be fruitful and lead to life in your marriage. It is true in marriage, however, that often we place expectations upon one another that are not God-ordained, but are personal preferences or desires.

Expectations, especially those that are unrealistic, can lead to misunderstanding and pain, while Godly assignments fulfilled will lead only to marital health and happiness.

Great Expectations

Steve Chapman, the Christian folk writer/singer said once, "The reason Annie and I have such a great marriage is because we expect so little of each other." The audience laughed, but as I thought about it later I realized how profound Steve's statement was. The vast majority of our conflicts in life resulting in hurt and anger, stem from unmet expectations. Expectations may be realistic, or absurd, but the end result of them not being met is still anger, which we must learn to handle rightly.

You pull into a fast food drive-thru and order your lunch. You're in a hurry (that's why you came to a *fast* food place). Time ticks by as the cars crawl toward the window. Finally your turn at the window arrives and the teen smiles and says, "Your order will be up in a few minutes. Just pull over there and we'll run it out to you." You feel the anger begin to rise. It's coming from an unmet expectation.

It's been a tough day at work. The boss yelled at you twice and your equipment broke down for over an hour. As you punch the clock you know you're headed home to your castle. Like a sanctuary surrounded by a moat, your home will be a place of tranquility and rest. Your loving wife will have a hot dinner ready, probably your favorite. The children will greet you with hugs and warm smiles. As soon as you pull in the drive your bubble is burst and your dream vanishes. Your wife is loading up the kids to head for soccer practice. She rolls down her window, yells something about a potpie in the fridge and blows you a kiss goodbye. Dejected, you go into a house that is a shambles and sorrow and rage begin to merge. Expectations: unmet!

Your husband never was Prince Charming, but he has been pretty good about responding to your needs. The washing machine, however, has been spinning out of whack for weeks. He promised he'd either fix it or get someone there who could. Today, however, he gave you his word. He said you could count on having it spinning like a top by 3 p.m. By 4 p.m. the only thing spinning is your head, with disappointment and anger picking up steam like a hurricane approaching the gulf. Another unmet expectation fuels the flames of conflict.

Tell about some unmet expectations that led to anger in your marriage: _____
_____
_____
_____
_____
_____
_____

Unmet expectations will come. They are a daily part of life. How we respond is critical. John Bevere in his book *Bait of Satan*, puts forth the position that Satan's primary tactic (or bait) to rob our life and destroy our witness is an offense. How we respond to an offense will determine whether we give way to anger and give room for Satan to do his destructive work — or if we choose to forgive and allow the offense to fall away harmlessly. Most offenses come from unmet expectations. That person said or did something I didn't think they should have, or they didn't say or do something I thought they should not have — so I am offended.

In a marriage, the opportunities for unmet expectations causing offenses come every day. These offenses open the door for anger. How a husband and wife deal with expectations is critical to the health of their marriage.

Taming The Turmoil
Here are a few suggestions to close the door on the adversary who would seek to destroy your marriage.

1. Maintain a balanced, realistic attitude about expectations. Steve Chapman gave seasoned wisdom when he implied that perhaps our expectations are too high. Give each other the benefit of the doubt. Seek to understand why the expectation was not met rather than to demand that your spouse understand your anger.

2. Be an unselfish servant, seeking to give rather than to receive. Selfishness and pride is at the core of offenses that come from unmet expectations. The more your world revolves around you, the more offenses you will find. When you grow into an attitude of seeking to serve rather than being served, you will find that your anger subsides.

3. Talk about expectations, avoid assumptions. Many unmet expectations are the product of assumptions that were not verbalized. Many times during marital counseling I've heard one of the partners say, "He never told me that was important to him" — or "she never said she expected that from me." Communication (which will be one whole session) can clarify expectations and foster harmony in the home.

4. Be ready to admit when you failed to meet a realistic expectation. Pride also hinders us from saying the words, "I was wrong. I'm sorry." A self-protective mechanism kicks in when we are accused and we immediately begin our defense. Be ready and willing to humbly admit you failed.

5. Set your heart to always forgive. Years ago I heard a sermon on the Lord's Prayer in which the preacher challenged us to set our heart at the beginning of the day to always forgive all offenses. That message changed my life. Even if your spouse does not admit you were wronged — even if they don't ask for forgiveness, go ahead and forgive and watch who walks away free. You do!

6. Don't let the sun go down on your anger. Elaine and I were counseled prior to our wedding to never go to bed — (or at least never go to sleep) angry. Satan is given opportunity when we let the sun set on our anger. Don't "sleep on it." It will turn into a nightmare. We've been up pretty late, but God has blessed us with the ability to always work through any offenses.

7. Grow through the conflict, being conformed to the image of Christ. Every time an offense has come my way, when I look in the mirror I see that God is chipping away some selfish pride in me. Quickly ask the question, "How can I (we) grow through this conflict?" Ask the Holy Spirit to speak the truth over the situation and you will see God transform both of you as you respond rightly.

Review the seven suggestions for overcoming the turmoil of unmet expectations. Of the seven:

Which did you find most helpful? _____
_____
_____

Which did you find most difficult to put into practice? _____
_____
_____
_____
_____

Personal expectations and God-given assignments are two different things. There are certain responsibilities and roles God has given to husbands and wives in the marital relations. Let's take a look into the Father's will for our marriages.

Nevertheless, each individual among you also is to love his own wife even as himself; and the wife must see to it that she respects her husband. — Ephesians 5:33

Orders From Heaven

The Hebrew custom to help remember a valuable truth was to write the main points in an acrostic. In other words the first letter of each main point spelled out a key word that brought the truths to mind. In our discussion of your unique roles, as husband and wife, we shall consider "R.E.S.P.E.C.T." for the wife and "C.H.E.R.I.S.H." for the husband. Ladies first.

R.E.S.P.E.C.T. Your Husband
(The Wife fills in these blanks)

R. The "R" is for respect. Since the scripture emphatically says, "see to it" that the wife respects her husband, then we must call attention to it. *Never* demean your husband. Treat him with honor. There may be times you feel he does not deserve your respect, but the Bible does not say to respect him when you feel he deserves it. Even in disagreement, show respect.

Do you respect your husband? _____ **Explain:** _____
_____
_____
_____

E. Encouragement is a real need of your husband. Woman was made from man's rib, the bone that guards his heart. You have a ministry of guarding your husband's heart with words of encouragement. Throughout his day he may receive criticism, but he needs encouraging words when he comes home to you.

Do you find it easy to say encouraging words to your husband? _____
Explain: _____
_____
_____

S. Submission is often misunderstood and resisted. First of all, the scriptures teach that both of you are to mutually submit to one another in the fear of Christ (Ephesians 5:21). The wife, however is told to submit to her husband. This means to let him lead. He is the head of the home, receiving your counsel, but ultimately responsible to lead.

What does submission mean to you? _____
_____
_____

P. Pray for your husband daily. Pray with your husband, verbally thanking God for him as you hold his hand. Pray for wisdom and strength. Bring specific concerns that face your husband to God in prayer.

Do you pray regularly for your husband? _____ **Explain:** _____
_____
_____

E. Exemplify Christ before your husband. Let him see Jesus in you. A powerful verse in 1 Peter reminds us that your example will speak louder to your husband than any words. "In the same way you wives, be submissive to your own husbands so that even if any of them are disobedient to the Word; they may be won without a word by the behavior of their wives" (1 Peter 3:1).

To what degree do you think you can live by 1 Peter 3:1?

0	1	2	3	4	5	6	7	8	9	10
No way					I'll try					You bet!

Explain: _____
_____

C. "C" is for counsel. In Genesis 2:18 God said, "It is not good for man to be alone; I will make a helper suitable for him." The word "helper" in Genesis is the same word used to describe the Holy Spirit in John 14:16. As the Holy Spirit gives counsel and direction, so a wife does for her husband. When you give counsel, don't nag. Give your husband time to consider his decisions and give God room to work.

How can you be a "helper" to your husband? _____
_____
_____

T. Transparent truthfulness displays respect. In almost every sitcom and in movies, you see women who are deceitful and manipulative. Lucy is always tricking Desi. Always be open and honest with your husband. Do not seek to manipulate him by deceptive measures.

Have you struggled with manipulating your husband? _____

Explain: _____
_____
_____

Of your God-given responsibilities (R.E.S.P.E.C.T.), which do you find most difficult to do?

Explain: _____
_____
_____
_____

C.H.E.R.I.S.H. Your Wife
(The husband responds to these)

C. The "C" reminds us of the Christ-like love you give to your wife. Ephesians 5:25 says to love your wife just as Christ loves the church. He died for us, didn't he? Not only must the husband be willing to die for his wife, he must be willing to live for her. Christ-like love is sacrificial. Put her needs ahead of your own.

Give an example of sacrificially loving your wife: _____
_____
_____

H. Honor her. She is your bride, your queen. Never speak words that would harm her or demean her. Often in courtship a man will open the door for his lady and show other expressions of polite honor. Too often, however, after the marriage she gets the door herself and he belches and pushes away from the table leaving the cleanup to her after a meal. Always honor her.

Tell of ways you can honor your bride: _____
_____
_____

E. Encouragement must come to the wife from the husband. In many instances where a woman is a stay-at-home mom with small children, she never hears an encouraging word throughout the day.

Do you find it easy to give encouraging words to your wife? _____
Explain: _____
_____

R. Refresh her. The husband is called the "groom." He has a ministry of grooming his wife to make her more radiant each day. Provide your wife times to rest and be refreshed. Refresh her with the Word of God. Ephesians 5:26 is a "grooming" picture: "that he might sanctify her, having cleansed her by the washing of water with the Word." Speak God's Word over her to bring refreshment to her.

Give an example of encouraging her with the Word: _____
_____
_____

I. Intercession is an important ministry of the husband. Intercession is praying on your wife's behalf as her advocate. Regularly pray protection and strength for your wife. Take the lead in prayer times together, speaking blessing out loud over your wife in prayer.

Do you pray regularly for your wife? _____ **Explain:** _____
_____
_____

S. Be a servant. Jesus was a King and he was a servant. You are both the head of this relationship and the servant. Look for opportunities to serve your wife. Don't put off fixing things that she needs repaired. Pick up your own dirty clothes and help with chores around the house.

Do you help around the house? _____ **How?** _____
_____
_____

H. The "H" is for husband. Be a husband for her. The word "husband" is made up of two words: "house" and "band." A house-band protects and provides security for his wife. He protects her from physical distress, emotional hardships, and spiritual attacks. Be alert to forces that would come against your wife and do what you can with God's help to defend her.

How can you protect your bride spiritually? _____
_____
_____

How can you protect your bride physically? _____
_____
_____

Of your God-given responsibilities (C.H.E.R.I.S.H.), which do you think you may find most difficult to do? Explain your answer: _____
_____
_____
_____

What you are given to do, you cannot do in your own strength. You need God's help. You need his grace and power by the Holy Spirit working in you and through you. Ask God to help you be the marriage partner he has called you to be.

Notes

Stop — Talk — And Listen, Listen, Listen

... But everyone must be quick to hear, slow to speak ...   — James 1:19

Rate your communication skills   0 1 2 3 4 5 6 7 8 9 10

Explain: _____
_____
_____

Rate the communication skills of your spouse: 0 1 2 3 4 5 6 7 8 9 10

Explain: _____
_____
_____

Good communication is essential to a successful, life-giving marriage. More than a mere exchange of words, communication is the expression of both information and emotions. It involves listening, talking, as well as body language. In the pre-marital video series, "So You're Getting Married," featuring Norman Wright, the following research data is shared:

> *Where there is one-on-one conversation — a couple having a face-to-face conver-sation — the message is conveyed in the following three ways:*
> 1. *Seven percent is the content itself. These are the actual words.*
> 2. *Thirty-eight percent is tone of voice. Our tone of voice has five times the impact of the actual words themselves.*
> 3. *Fifty-five percent of communication is non-verbal, or what is referred to as body language. In communication the eyes are often more important than the ears.*

The "total person" is involved in communication. As you relate to your spouse, make every effort to be fully engaged in the communication connection.

Communication Exercise: Take turns at this. Tell your spouse what you remember about your first date, briefly please.

Listener Notes
1. Summarize the content of what your spouse related to you.

_____
_____
_____
_____
_____

2. What did his/her tone of voice say to you as the recollection of the first date was shared?

_____
_____
_____
_____

3. What did his/her body language convey to you as your spouse shared.

_____
_____
_____
_____

Speaker Notes
Rate your spouse as a listener as you shared your thoughts about your first date.

0	1	2	3	4	5	6	7	8	9	10

What did his/her body language communicate to you as he/she listened to you?

_____
_____
_____
_____

James reminded us in his brief epistle that listening was a priority over speaking (James 1:19). God gave us two ears and only one mouth, so perhaps he was trying to get us to do twice as much listening as talking.

When you are engaged in conversations with your spouse, make every effort to listen with your whole self.

1. Listen with your ears. Pay close attention to the actual content of the words that are being related to you. If a radio, television, children, or other sounds distract you, take steps to curb the distractions. Taking those steps will communicate to your spouse that you genuinely want to hear what he or she has to say.

List some sound distractions that occur when the two of you attempt to have conversation. What solutions have you found to resolve distractions?

_____
_____
_____
_____

2. Listen with your eyes. Wandering eyes speak a message of disinterest. Eyes that have become fixed with a glassy glare shout boredom. Rolling your eyes sends signals of disapproval. Make every effort to be both respectful and attentive with your eyes. Always look at your spouse when he or she is speaking to you.

Rate yourself as to whether you are a good "eye" listener.

0   1   2   3   4   5   6   7   8   9   10

Explain: _____

_____

_____

Rate your spouse as to whether he or she is a good "eye" listener.

0   1   2   3   4   5   6   7   8   9   10

Explain: _____

_____

_____

3. Listen with your body. Stop squirming. Don't slump your shoulders proclaiming, "Do I have to listen to this?" Be attentive even with your posture. Facial expressions can be great ways to communicate you are really listening.

Tell about a time your spouse's body language "gave them away" as to how they really felt about what you were saying.

_____

_____

_____

_____

4. Listen with your mind. Jesus said that those who had ears to hear would hear his words. As far as we know everyone listening had ears. Have you ever had someone say to you, "Do you hear what I'm saying?" What they are asking is whether the words are making contact with your brain — are you understanding? A spouse can tell when your ears are there but your mind is a million miles away. Some of us have the problem that the wheels of our mind begin to formulate our response before we've heard all that our mate has to say, so we miss vital information. Be sure your mind is engaged in the conversation.

Do you struggle with mental focus when it comes to conversations with your spouse?

___ yes   ___ no   ___ some

Explain: _____

_____

_____

_____

5. Listen with your heart. One time, Elaine and I were talking on the phone and all of her words communicated that everything was fine. However, there were tones and inflections that sent signals to my heart that not everything was fine. I stopped her and said, "Are you really okay?" Listen with your heart intently to the emotions that are being communicated to you.

Tell about a recent conversation with your spouse in which you picked up on an emotional signal that did not come from the content of the words.

_____
_____
_____
_____

6. Listen with your mouth. That may seem like an odd listening tool, but it is a great instrument of clarification. Most people like feedback and questions. Both are expressions of interest. A question like, "Do I understand correctly that you are saying?" or "How do you feel about that?" With your words you can take the conversation to deeper levels of understanding. Be careful not to cut your spouse off — nor take over the conversation.

Write down three to five good questions you can ask during a conversation to demonstrate interest and to take the topic deeper.
1. _____
2. _____
3. _____
4. _____
5. _____

Listening is an art, one that will be skillfully developed as you grow to understand your spouse. We learn and grow far more from listening than talking. Listen well to one another and your relationship will be strong and vibrant.

Talking With One Another

> _Let no unwholesome word proceed from your mouth, but only such a word as is good for edification according to the need of the moment, so that it may give grace to those who hear._
> — Ephesians 4:29

Words are powerful. Several years ago I did a children's sermon about words. I squeezed toothpaste out on my finger then asked the children if they thought I could get it back in. They all agreed I could not. I told them that words were like that. Once they are out, they are out. I then wiped the toothpaste off my finger and had the children smell my "minty" finger. I told them that even though the toothpaste was now gone — it left an odor behind. Often with unkind words, even when we've asked forgiveness, there is a residue of hurt that may remain.

Tell about some words you spoke that you wish you had not said: _____
_____
_____
_____
_____

Guard Your Tongue

Proverbs 13:3 says, "The one who guards his mouth preserves his life; the one who opens wide his lips comes to ruin." David penned these words in Psalm 34: "Keep your tongue from evil and your lips from speaking deceit" (v.13). As you read at the beginning of this session, the Apostle Paul wrote, "Let no unwholesome word proceed from your mouth" (Ephesians 4:29a). Make every effort to control your tongue.

A wise old woman told me once, "Be sure to engage your brain before shooting off your mouth." In other words, think before you speak.

The tongue is one of the most difficult body parts to control. James said, "Every species of beasts and birds, of reptiles and creatures of the sea is tamed and has been tamed by the human race. But no one can tame the tongue; it is a restless evil and full of deadly poison." Those are strong words declaring how difficult it is for us to control our words.

> *A fellow came to his pastor once confessing he had a terrible problem with cursing. He said, "Pastor, I just can't control it. The words just slip out all the time. What am I going to do?" The pastor smiled and said, "Why Bill, I've never heard you curse." "Of course not, pastor. I'd never curse around you!" "Then you can control it. You have controlled it around me."*

On a scale of 1-10 (10 being "Great"), rate how well you do at controlling your tongue.

    0   1   2   3   4   5   6   7   8   9   10

Explain your response: _____
_____
_____
_____
_____

There would not be so many commands in scripture challenging us to "take control" when it comes to our words if it were not possible for us to exercise wise restraint. Think before you speak — and seek to speak words that bring life.

The Tongue/Heart Connection

Did you know the tongue is connected to your heart, and that many of your "word" problems are actually heart failure? Jesus said, "You brood of vipers, how can you, being evil, speak what is good? *For the mouth speaks out of that which fills the heart.* The good man brings out of his good treasure what is good; and the evil man brings out of his evil treasure what is evil. But I tell you that every *careless* word that people speak they shall give an accounting for it in the Day of Judgment. For by your words you will be justified, and by your words you will be condemned."

Careless words are the ones you didn't think about before you spoke them. Jesus was saying that those careless words reveal what's really in the heart as they "slip out." That is why those words receive stricter judgment. Listen to a mouth talk long enough and you will discover what fills the heart.

If I came home from work talking about Gertrude (that is a made up name), raving about her skills, her beauty, her personality, discussing her daily actions and activities, I think my wife, Elaine, would begin to wonder about my feelings for Gertrude. If it went on for days or weeks, Elaine would come to the conclusion that Gertrude held an inappropriate place in my heart because my mouth was always talking about her. Elaine would be right.

If you find yourself consistently speaking words to your spouse that hurt — or if you rarely give words that encourage or assure your mate of your affections, you don't just have a "word" problem. There is a heart problem. If you are constantly critical or cynical in your speech, there is a heart issue that needs resolved.

Many marriages have suffered deep decay because of hurtful words, or lack of caring, nurturing words because a heart has become dirty or calloused. It's not time to attempt to "muscle up" and talk rightly to one another. It is time to cry out to God as King David did when he said, "Create in me a clean heart and renew a right spirit in me" (Psalm 51:10).

Perhaps because of past disappointments, hurtful words or actions, unforgiveness or bitterness your heart has been filled with vile stuff that spills out on your spouse. It may even be that much of the "evil" that stains your heart and taints your words has little or nothing to do with your spouse, but comes from your past — or from other relationships. The source of the stain matters little — the solution is still the same. Call upon the Lord to forgive you. Confess your sin and ask God to forgive and *cleanse* you of all unrighteousness.

Pause For Prayer

Take a moment right now to ask the Holy Spirit to show you any "hurtful" way in your heart. Confess any bitterness, lust, jealousy, anger, or similar feelings, and ask God to forgive and cleanse you. Talk with your spouse about your time of prayer.

The heart is at the heart of the matter when it comes to our words, yet we do have a responsibility to control our words. Getting our heart right is one of the best controls. Secondly, taking time to pray (and think) before we speak allows God to set a guard about your lips. Third, you do need to exercise discretion and self-control.

Here are a few "talking tips" as you communicate with one another:

1. **Don't dominate the conversation.** Seek more to hear than to be heard. Avoid only talking about your interests.
2. **Strive to speak words that will be positive and life giving.** Be sure criticism is constructive.
3. **Never use demeaning words or name-calling.** Using words like stupid and dumb is a stupid, dumb thing to do.
4. **Speak often of your love and appreciation for your spouse.** Brag about your mate to others.
5. **Yelling is a "telling" sign that you are out of control.** Keep your composure.
6. **Be sensitive about timing as when to talk about specific issues.** Don't bring up having more children right after your wife has delivered.
7. **Be sure your spouse has heard you — and has received the correct information.**
8. **Always be fully truthful.** Don't leave out significant parts of the story attempting to keep the truth from your spouse. While you're not lying, it is deceitfulness.
9. **Avoid hinting, implicating, and being manipulative.** Be open, honest, telling it like it is.
10. **Talk about feelings as well as information.** Remember, words reveal your heart. Let it show.

Of the 10 tips, which do you find most difficult to do? Explain: _____
_____
_____
_____
_____
_____
_____
_____
_____
_____
_____

Communication is so foundational to a good marriage. You can be a good listener and you can become an even better one with Christ's help. You can speak words that are life-giving as the Lord of life fills your heart. Set your heart and mind to grow in your communication with one another.

Notes

In Pursuit Of Understanding

So, as those who have been chosen of God, holy and beloved, put on a heart of compassion, kindness, humility, gentleness and patience; bearing with one another, and forgiving each other, whoever has a complaint against anyone; just as the Lord forgave you, so also should you. Beyond all these things put on love, which is the perfect bond of unity.   — Colossians 3:12-14

Love is patient, love is kind and is not jealous; love does not brag and is not arrogant, does not act unbecomingly; it does not seek its own, is not provoked, does not take into account a wrong suffered, does not rejoice in unrighteousness, but rejoices with the truth; [love] bears all things, believes all things, hopes all things, endures all things. Love never fails ...   — 1 Corinthians 13:4-8a

Love is never a mere emotion in scripture. It is clear that love is a decision — a commitment. Love chooses to be patient, unselfish, forgiving, and understanding. While love is an act of our will, it is clearly a work of God in our lives. It is the fruit of the Holy Spirit (Galatians 5:22). Of ourselves we could never "muster" the kind of selfless love described in the passages in Colossians or Corinthians. Only surrendering to the leading of the Holy Spirit will bring about true love.

A mark of love is that we "bear with one another." We are patient with each other. In other words, we work harder at understanding one another than being understood by the other. In marriage, understanding one another is a vital key to satisfaction and success.

To what degree do you feel like your spouse understands you?

    0   1   2   3   4   5   6   7   8   9   10

Explain: _____

_____

_____

To what degree do you feel like you understand your spouse?

    0   1   2   3   4   5   6   7   8   9   10

Explain: _____

_____

_____

We're All Different

Perhaps you've noticed that not only are men and women different, people are different. I heard a man say once, "We are all unique, just like everyone else." We can allow those differences to be a constant source of irritation, or we can utilize them to enable us to grow and become more like Christ.

Differences are sort of like "holy sandpaper" God will use to refine us and conform us to the image of his Son (Romans 8:29).

> *When I was a young pastor I was very impulsive. I wanted to be a "mover" and a "shaker." I had on our church board a couple of elders who were "immovable" and "unshakable." They resisted every change I proposed. I was convinced they were tools of the enemy to keep our church from doing the will of God. I went so far as to see them as adversaries. I'll never forget the night prior to a board meeting, God gently impressed on my heart to begin to listen to these older men, seek to understand them, and give thanks for their counsel. Suddenly I began to view them as a "check and balance," refining my impulsive heart. From that night on God began building a dynamic team.*

In your marriage you will have significant differences as individuals. You can choose to have those differences serve to build you as a team — or allow them to alienate you. Seek to understand one another, accentuating the positive in your differences and give God plenty of room to refine and transform both of you to be more like Jesus.

Some Common Uncommon Ground

We're going to take a look at a few areas where people experience significant differences. Before we do, let me make a couple of disclaimers and some clarifications.

1. **Differences between individuals are multiple and complex.** Volumes have been written about how people think and act differently. Our gender, background, experiences, genetic code, and environment are all factors in who we are and what we are like. It is impossible to capture the full ramifications of the complexity of these differences in one session. However, this can serve as a place to get us started thinking about our individual uniqueness, considering the positive outcome God intends.

2. **The differences we will consider will only be dealt with in a summary fashion.** (Check out the references if you want to dig deeper.) There are numerous resources dealing at length with each of the topics we will merely scan. In our brief encounter with the topic, you may discover it would be helpful for your marriage to pursue the subject further.

3. **Avoid seeking to "pigeonhole" your spouse as you review the differences.** We are speaking in generalities. There are always exceptions. Remember, our goal is to understand, not to restrict.

4. **Approach these differences in a non-judgmental manner.** As you read about these differences, there is not a right and a wrong — a better or a worse. They are simply differences. They are differences not only to be understood, but also to be appreciated.

5. Focus in on the final section in this material addressing the issue of "how to grow through differences." Set your hearts now as a couple to make the most of your uniqueness to experience the greatest pleasure and bring glory to God.

The differences we will consider include: birth order, temperament, love languages, and gender.

Birth Order (Primary Resource: *The Birth Order Book* by Kevin Leman)
Generally speaking, the order you were born in your family can have a significant influence on who you are. Keep in mind there are many variables that can change the generalities. For example, if you come from a family of four children, yet there were ten years between child two and three, child three will probably display many firstborn tendencies as well as some middle child characteristics. Gender will also influence birth order tendencies. A third born male with two older sisters will demonstrate last born or "baby" characteristics, but may also display some firstborn nature as the first male. Keeping in mind that variables will influence birth order tendencies, there are generalities that can help us understand one another.

General Characteristics

Firstborn & Only Child	Middle Child	Last Born / Baby
perfectionist	mediator	manipulative
reliable	avoids conflict	charming
conscientious	independent	blames others
list maker	loyalty to peers	shows off
well-organized	many friends	people person
critical	maverick	good sales person
serious	unpredictable	precocious
scholarly	display first and last characteristics	engaging

Why does this matter in a marriage?
Elaine is a firstborn. I am a "baby." Even in preparing for our wedding I noticed her lists. As we approached our wedding day, she was moving resolutely toward a well-orchestrated event. I was headed to a party. I planned the honeymoon. What that means is I bought plane tickets to Boston. What happened the next ten days was "off the cuff." No reservations made — just hop in the car and head for Maine. We certainly learned a lot on our honeymoon.

Then someone who loved us pointed us to *The Birth Order Book*. I scanned it, in true last born fashion, but I caught the significance of the truth within the pages. I began to understand my firstborn wife and resisted judging her ways that were so foreign to me. (Being a firstborn, who by nature is critical — it took her longer to stop judging my "baby" ways.)

Believe it or not, I now find myself making lists — and calling ahead for reservations. (I still have trouble asking for directions, but that's another issue.) Elaine, on the other hand, is more spontaneous, less critical, and wrestles less with perfectionism. God has used our differences to sand off some rough spots. Knowing our birth order differences has also led to greater understanding and joy. Knowing it helps Elaine relax and enjoy a vacation more with a list, a schedule, and reservations, we process all those things together, building in allowance for spontaneity. Vacations are a lot more fun for all of us now. Even how we raise the children is influenced by our birth order, and understanding those differences leads to unity and peace.

As a general rule, same birth combinations in a marriage are more likely to have struggles.

Please remember: 1) with Christ all things are possible; 2) these are generalities; and, 3) any marriage takes work to be all God wants it to be.

Two firstborns — or especially two "only child" individuals can see some strong-willed conflict. Given over to the flesh rather than to the Holy Spirit, two firstborns can literally nitpick each other apart. Two middle-borns can be so set on avoiding conflict that they never get to the real issues of their marriage. A couple of babies can be so charming and free they soon find their home life a wreck, burdened down with astronomical financial debt.

What is your birth order in your family?

_____

Mention any unusual influences that might affect your birth order tendencies.

_____

_____

Generally speaking, do the characteristics listed early in this session resonate with you?

_____

_____

Do the characteristics listed seem to describe your spouse? _____

_____

_____

Tell how understanding the significance of birth order can enhance your marriage. Be specific. _____

_____

_____

_____

Temperament (Primary Resource: *Spirit Controlled Temperaments* by Tim LaHaye)
Each of us has inborn, God-given traits that affect how we respond to life. Tim LaHaye has written extensively on temperaments, including books dealing with the importance of allowing the Holy Spirit to transform those temperaments. In every way, God wants to work positively with those traits with which he has "graced" us.

Let me clarify by saying that temperament is not the same as character or personality. Dr. LaHaye expresses it this way, "temperament is the combination of traits we are born with (it's in your genetic design), character is our 'civilized' temperament; and personality is the 'face' we show to others."

It is helpful for understanding and the building of oneness in a marriage to have some grasp of our own unique temperament traits as well as those of our spouse. The Father will create a masterpiece in your marriage as your unique traits interact and refine each other.

In summary, there are four basic temperaments, each with both strengths and weaknesses. Typically every individual has one dominant temperament and one secondary. Let me remind you, there is no temperament that is *right* or *better* and another *wrong* or *worse*. They are different. Understanding these differences in a non-judgmental manner is our goal.

	Strengths	**Weaknesses**
Sanguine	enjoying	restless
	optimistic	weak-willed
	friendly	egotistical
	compassionate	emotionally unstable
Choleric	strong willpower	hot-tempered
	practical	cruel
	leader	impetuous
	optimistic	self-sufficient
Melancholy	sensitive	self-centered
	perfectionist	pessimistic
	analytical	moody
	faithful	revengeful
	self-sacrificing	
Phlegmatic	witty	slow/lazy
	dependable	tease
	practical	stubborn
	efficient	indecisive

As you review the strengths and weakness of each temperament, self-examination will be of greater value than spousal-examination. Focus more on what God has created in you and how that can be channeled for the greatest good in your life and in your marriage.

Review the list and seek to understand the temperament of your mate. Understanding the temperament of your spouse enables you to pray for and encourage your spouse as he or she becomes more like Christ.

In your life and in your marriage, the Holy Spirit is working to conform you to the image of Christ. Remember as a Christian you are "re-born" — or born again, with a new genetic code displacing the old. You are a new creation. While rebirth is a one-time event, the transformation is a process.

As God works in and through your relationship with one another — and through his Holy Spirit, the positive characteristics of your inborn nature blend with the even more powerful traits of the Holy Spirit: love, joy, peace, patience, kindness, goodness, faithfulness, gentleness, and self-control. God miraculously is conforming maturity, "to the measure of the stature which belongs to the fullness of Christ" (Ephesians 4:13c).

List what you consider to be your temperament strengths:

_____
_____
_____
_____

What areas do you recognize the Holy Spirit is still strong at work transforming?

_____
_____
_____
_____

Love Languages (Primary Resource: *The Five Love Languages* by Gary Chapman)
Gary Chapman, author of the book, *The Five Love Languages*, was very influential in the enrichment of our marriage. The main thesis of Chapman's book is that each of us speaks one predominant "love language" and that same language is also primarily how we receive love.

If someone from Mexico came up to me and told me how much he appreciated me — what a great guy I am — really heaping on the compliments, I wouldn't have a clue as to whether he was calling me a hero or a pickup truck. Because we would be communicating in two very different languages, we would not connect.

Besides the verbal language we speak, we each speak a love language (often more than one — but usually one or two predominantly). A love language is an expression of endearment or affection.

According to Dr. Chapman, there are five basic love languages:
1. **Words of Affirmation**: Compliments, encouraging words, kind, and humble words
2. **Quality Time**: Being together, sharing conversations, listening, asking questions
3. **Gift Giving**: Remembering special occasions, sometimes-extravagant gifts for no special occasion
4. **Acts of Service**: Helping around the house, fixing a great meal
5. **Physical Touch**: hugs, sitting close, hand on shoulder

For some, saying, "I love you means," spending time together. To another it means cleaning your house for you. For many, love is demonstrated through the gifts of flowers, perfume, or tools. Just holding hands whispers love to another. Words of encouragement assure some they are loved. Understanding the love language of your spouse is a vital part of expressing love to him or her.

> *My predominant love language is service. Elaine's is quality time. I would come home from work and immediately look for opportunities to serve. I would start doing the dishes, or picking up around the house. Meanwhile, she would try to pull me into a conversation that distracted me from my serving. I was speaking my love language and she was speaking hers, but we were two ships passing in the night.*

When I discovered what language Elaine was speaking (and needed to hear), I started taking time to spend quality time with her. When she learned that serving was my language, she understood my passion to "help" and began to hear the "I love you" in my serving. She also looked for opportunities to serve so I would hear her love expressions.

From this our marriage has deepened and we've both learned a new language. It can cause serious decay in your marriage if the two of you are not speaking the same love language — or if you don't understand the language that assures your spouse of your love.

One of the great dangers of being unaware of your spouse's love language is if he or she does not hear it, your spouse begins to feel rejected and unloved. You may be shouting, "I love you" in your language, but if your spouse knows only another language, you are a noisy gong. In other words, if your spouse hears "I love you" through the vehicle of gifts, but you think gifts are a waste — or too materialistic — and quality time is true love, you will probably never speak the language your spouse needs to hear to know of your love. In fact, you may shun the gifts your mate has given you since that is not your language, inadvertently spurning her or his love.

What do you think is your spouse's love language? (Can be two)

_____

_____

What do you think is your love language? (Can be two)

_____

_____

On a scale of 1-10 rate how well you do as a couple at speaking and hearing each other's love language.

0	1	2	3	4	5	6	7	8	9	10

Explain: _____

_____

_____

Love Languages Transformed

Since I read Dr. Chapman's book, I've learned a couple of new love languages. Not only have I learned to speak them, I've also come to enjoy receiving them. I'm out to learn all five.

Even in my pursuit to learn all five languages, I realize it is only possible with Christ for me to grasp all five languages fluently. He is the source of real love. Jesus spoke all five languages so perfectly — and as Christ is perfected in me, his love will be manifested through me.

Work hard to understand the love language of your spouse. Make every effort to speak the language that assures your mate of your care and commitment. But above all, call on Christ to fill your heart with his all encompassing, overwhelming love.

Gender

A few years ago *TIME* magazine came out with an earth-shaking cover story. The headlines read, "Researchers Find That Men and Women Are Different." (I wondered how many government dollars were invested to come up with that nugget of profound truth.) The Bible gives a very clear picture that the sexes are different. Understanding those differences is an avenue to delight in your marriage. Let's consider only a few. (We will deal with physical/sexual differences in the session on intimacy.) Again, we will address these issues in generalities. There are always exceptions.

Women Are Shoppers — Men Are Hunters

Elaine can go to the mall all day, come home with nothing and have had success. Her success is even sweeter if she spent the day with a friend. I go after what I need, find it, and I'm ready to head home. We have learned to meet in the middle when it comes to shopping. I now enjoy just being with my wife at the mall. She is sensitive to my male limitations when it comes to browsing.

Have you experienced the shopper/hunter conflict in your marriage? ___ yes ___ no

Explain: _____

_____

_____

Women Are Conversationalists — Men Relay Information

Women want every detail when they ask the question, "How was your day?" Men are content to simply say, "Fine." Conversation is an expression of genuine care for a woman. She loves for the husband to ask questions. She longs for deep conversations of both information and emotions.

Which of the two of you is more talkative? _____

To what degree are your conversational needs met in your mate?

0   1   2   3   4   5   6   7   8   9   10

Explain: _____

_____

_____

Men Are Goal Centered — Women Are Relational

If a group of women were in a huddle as a football team, they would probably get called for delay of game because they are checking out how everyone is doing. The play may go nowhere, but they will encourage one another as they return to the huddle. Men on the other hand, break out of that huddle headed for the goal line. They don't need to know each other's name — or any other details. They have a mission.

In planning a vacation, it is more important to the wife "how" the family arrives — and the interaction in the vehicle, rather than the shortest, fastest route.

Have you found goal grasping and relational building to cause conflict in your marriage?

___ yes   ___ no

Explain: _____
_____
_____

Men Are Stone Pots — Women Are Fragile Vases

1 Peter 3:7 says, "You husbands in the same way, live with your wives in an understanding way, as with someone weaker, since she is a woman, and show her honor as a fellow heir of the grace of life." Women are not lesser, but like an expensive vase, they are more fragile than men. They are more prone to be emotionally upset.

> *Early in our marriage I knew Elaine was a better bookkeeper than I was. We agreed she would pay the bills and balance the checkbook. I observed it becoming a heavy strain upon her. I sensed the Lord telling me it was not for her to bear. I took over the checkbook and took that burden from her.*

Men are to live with their wives in an understanding way. While women should do the same with their husbands, they are never commanded to do so in scripture. Why? Because man is to be the primary protector and emotional burden bearer for his fragile wife.

What does it mean to you when the scripture says the wife is the weaker vessel?
_____
_____
_____
_____

What other gender differences do you face as a couple? _____
_____
_____
_____
_____

Dynamically Dealing With The Differences

Here are a few tips to make the most of the unique attributes each of you bring to the marriage.

L ook in the mirror when the differences irritate you. Generally I have found that when something about Elaine gets under my skin — it's my skin that God is adjusting. Avoid judging or criticizing your spouse — instead, take personal inventory and see what God is working in you.

O ptimize every opportunity for growth. Differences are not obstacles in your marriage. They are opportunities for God to be glorified and for you to be transformed. Pray for one another. Encourage one another. Affirm the positive aspects of those differences.

V igorously seek to understand your spouse. I know I have said this several times but it is so key to having a life-giving marriage. Understanding is an avenue to delight and fruitfulness in your marriage.

E ncourage and exhort one another into Christ-likeness! There are some real negatives about my baby birth order and my sanguine temperament. I am grateful to God that Elaine has lovingly encouraged me to rise above some of the "dark sides" of our differences. By her example and through prayer, God has worked to expand the positive.

Here we are back to that word "love" again. Love decides to be patient — to bear with one another — to not seek its own — to understand. Yes, as Paul said, "Love is the perfect bond of unity."

Notes

Finding A Firm Financial Foundation

An overwhelming majority of couples that have divorced will say financial conflicts were a major part of the cause of their marital failure. Money, or the lack thereof, can be the fuel for many family feuds. It does not need to be this way. When our finances are in order, following biblical guidelines, there is peace.

Finance Quiz

Be sure to do this work on your own. If you are unsure of an answer, go ahead and guess. Wait until the session together to compare your responses.

Tell approximately how much you spend on average each month for the following categories:

Category	Monthly Expense	Reponse of Spouse Complete in Session
Food	_____	_____
Rent/House payment	_____	_____
Utilities (gas, electric, water)	_____	_____
Phone	_____	_____
Clothing	_____	_____
Insurance (car, home, health, life)	_____	_____
Entertainment	_____	_____
Gasoline	_____	_____
Auto (payment, upkeep)	_____	_____
Misc. (toiletries, cleaning supplies, laundry)	_____	_____
Church/Charities	_____	_____
TOTAL	_____	_____

As you reviewed your monthly financial commitments, were both of you informed as to what you actually face? Were you in agreement as to the amounts? Is there enough income to meet the monthly expenses? Review your budget together on a regular basis so your both remain informed and in unity.

To what degree are you adequately aware of all of your financial commitments?

0   1   2   3   4   5   6   7   8   9   10

Explain: _____

_____

To what degree are you in unity when it comes to financial issues?

0   1   2   3   4   5   6   7   8   9   10

Explain: _____

_____

_____

Mastering Money

As we consider financial issues in this session, let me encourage you that money is not the real issue. The issue is your heart — and your relationship with God.

> *For the love of money is a root of all sorts of evil, and some by longing for it have wandered away from the faith and pierced themselves with many griefs. But flee from these things, you man of God, and pursue righteousness, godliness, faith, love, perseverance and gentleness.* — 1 Timothy 6:10-11

Have you been pierced with many a pang pursuing pennies? Has the love of money caused a wrestling in your life — or in your marriage? Money and other things of this world have a strong allure to become central in our lives. Too often we buy the lie that if we just had more "stuff" we would have more happiness, peace, and contentment. Jesus is to be Lord of every area of our lives, including our finances and he is the source of our peace, joy, and contentment.

> *No one can serve two masters; for either he will hate the one and love the other, or he will be devoted to one and despise the other. You cannot serve God and wealth.* — Matthew 6:24

Money is not a problem by itself. When we struggle with the love of money the real issue is a heart problem. Who is master of our lives? Are our hearts surrendered to God, allowing him to give the directives in all aspects of our lives?

A master or lord is one who gives the orders. He guides and motivates those in subjection to him. Does God guide and motivate your life or is your motivation the pursuit of material gain? Do you do what you do because you know it is what God wants — or because it seems like the best way to make money and have financial security?

To what degree do you wrestle with serving money rather than God?

0	1	2	3	4	5	6	7	8	9	10
Money is winning out!					Both a bit					God is #1

Explain: _____

_____

_____

The love of money or material things can rob you of your relationship with your spouse, but more importantly, it can rob you of your walk with Christ. As a couple, set your hearts to put material things in their proper perspective.

Caretaker Couples

> *God blessed them; and God said to them, "Be fruitful and multiply, and fill the earth, and subdue it; and rule over the fish of the sea and over the birds of the sky and over every living thing that moves on the earth."* — Genesis 1:28

From the beginning God put the human race on planet earth as caretakers of all the "stuff" that is here. It all belongs to God, but he has entrusted us to manage and care for his creation. A term we use often in the church is the word "steward." A steward is a manager or overseer. We are to be good stewards of God's creation.

In the area of finances we are called to be good stewards, faithful caretakers of God's provision. We must remember it is all his and we are entrusted to administrate well what he has given us. We maintain a healthy biblical perspective when we remember we are God's careful caretakers of his precious provision.

> *I served a rural church for seven years in Northwest Missouri. Those farmers taught me much about faith and stewardship. One older farmer told me of the day he made his final mortgage payment. (That's a big deal for a farmer!) He walked out into the center of his fields and boasted to himself, "It's all mine!" As soon as he had uttered those words he sensed the Spirit of the Lord speak back to him saying, "That's what the last owner said, too. Remember, my son, it's all mine!" The farmer fell to his knees and wept. His tears were a mixture of both remorse and gratitude. He was sorry for his arrogance and grateful for God's gentle hand to put things back in perspective.*

Do you, as a couple, understand you are stewards, or caretakers of what God has entrusted to you?

___ yes   ___ sort of   ___ no

Explain: _____

_____

_____

Fatal Financial Flaws

The thief comes only to steal and kill and destroy; I came that they might have life, and have it abundantly.
— John 10:10

Jesus came to give us life in every area of our lives, including our finances. If we are to be good and fruitful stewards of the things of God we cannot allow the thief (Satan) to steal, kill, and destroy even our material possessions.

I do not mean God wants us rich. I am not proclaiming a gospel of financial prosperity. There is a principle of fruitfulness and life that permeates the scriptures. Whether we have little or much, God desires good fruit to come from what we have. In the realm of our finances we are to experience the reality of *life-giving*, rather than life-consuming. Money and other material possessions are to be utilized as godly tools to see the kingdom of God extended. Money can provide great avenues to glorify God, as well as meet your basic human needs.

The reality is that far too many Christians find themselves in frequent financial crisis. Debt, worry, and covetousness (craving what we do not have) plague our attitudes and actions. Why do so many couples get into financial bondage and disarray, leading to frustration and fruitlessness?

There are some common pitfalls couples experience which lead to financial frustrations. Here are the pitfalls — and the solutions.

1. **Failure to have a budget or maintain one defeats many.** A budget is a financial target that keeps us on course to achieve godly goals. If we have no budget we most certainly will miss the mark of being fruitful stewards. If we have a budget, but ignore it, we are no better off. If you want to walk in financial freedom, the place to begin is for you and your spouse to establish a God-guided budget and live by it.

   Do you have a realistic, workable budget? ___ yes ___ no ___ sort of

   Do you live by it? Explain your answer. ___ yes ___ no ___ sort of

   _____

   _____

   _____

Solution: Set up a budget and live by it. If you have trouble getting started with the budget process, let me suggest you call **Crown Financial Ministry Inc.** at 1-800-722-1976 and order *The Financial Planning Organizer*. My family has faithfully functioned with this budget system with great success. Be sure your budget is realistic and mutually acceptable.

When you get a budget developed, resolve to live by it. It will be a difficult discipline at first, but it will lead to financial freedom in the long run.

2. **"Keeping up with the Joneses" lures many of us into financial difficulties.** We want the latest computer, car, CD player, or whatever it is the neighbors just got. Peer pressure doesn't only work on teens. How often do we ignore our budget or the prompting of the Holy Spirit because we are seeking to maintain the latest trends?

Tell of a recent purchase that was motivated by peer pressure:

_____

_____

_____

Solution: Just say "no" to peer pressure when it comes to those unplanned expenditures. Don't covet any of your neighbor's stuff and don't sabotage your budget to get what your neighbor has.

3. **Poor planning plagues many.** Property taxes come due every year, yet how many people seem surprised by them? Your car will need new tires some day. Why do I hear Christians say, "We're really in a crunch right now, we had to buy new tires!" We can anticipate many expenses and set aside provisions for them. Plan ahead!

Discuss your financial planning:

_____

_____

_____

_____

Solution: Set aside funds for further expenses. We set aside $50 per month for Christmas gifts. We put $100 per month in savings for property tax and insurance. I met with a couple once and suggested they set aside $40 per month for their car insurance. They said they couldn't afford to. I asked them if they could afford the $500 on January 1 when the premium came due. They admitted that the insurance payment always sent them into a financial tailspin and forced them to live on credit cards. Credit is not the solution! Planning and laying aside the provision within our means is the key.

4. **Are you an "impulse" consumer?** Before we got on a budget I would always come out of the store with something that was not on my list. When the telemarketing person calls, are you prone to making hasty purchases? Impulse spending can set your finances into total disarray.

What was your latest impulse purchase?

_____

_____

Solution: Never exceed your budget. Resist impulsive purchases. Having a budget has made it easy for me to say to those telemarketing agents that what they are promoting doesn't fit within our budget. It also keeps me focused when I go into any store.

5. **Credit cards come too easily and are too easy to use.** Debt, especially debt incurred on a credit card, is bondage. The bill always comes due. If you do not fully anticipate the ability to pay off that credit card each month, you must seriously consider the appropriateness of its usage.

I have seen far too many young couples, and some older couples, over their heads in debt because of easy credit card access. Watch out for the credit card trap!

Is credit card debt a problem for you? ___ yes ___ no

Explain: _____

_____

_____

Solution: If you cannot control yourself when it comes to credit cards, I suggest you destroy them. Debt is bondage. Credit cards, however, are not the real problem. The person signing the ticket is the problem.

> *We use a credit card which has no annual fee and pays a percentage per purchase. Each time we use the credit card, we record it in our checkbook and subtract it from our balance just as if we had written a check. When I pay the credit card bill, I have nothing to subtract, pay no interest and receive a monthly bonus. Last year we received a check for nearly $200 for using our credit card.*

Just as money is not the root of all evil, credit cards are not the root of financial bondage.

6. **Discerning *needs* from *wants* is a struggle for us all.** A key to financial stability is the ability to distinguish needs from wants. I have seen people who have a difficult time getting food on the table, yet they keep their cable television bill current or zip into McDonald's on a regular basis. Have you diligently sought to distinguish your needs from your wants?

Tell about how you have prioritized your spending:

_____

_____

_____

_____

Solution: Prioritize your spending according to biblical guidelines. Needs come before wants. Prayerfully let God have leadership in your finances.

7. **Sinful habits can bring havoc to your financial health.** Overeating, purchasing, illegal drugs, gambling, or addiction to pornography are just a few sinful habits that are costly and erosive to the family finances. Impulsive spending can be equally destructive. Failure to use finances according to biblical directives, such as tithing, can bring financial instability. Sin has a high price, both spiritually and materially.

Is there some sin habit that is draining your financial resources?   ___ yes   ___ no

If you answered yes, can you talk about your answer?

_____

_____

_____

_____

Solution: Repent of sinful habits that are robbing you of financial stability. Seek counsel from your pastor or other spiritual advisor as to what portions of your income might be going to items that do not glorify God or bring life to you and your family. You may need to seek assistance to overcome destructive habits that are eroding your financial security.

8. **Crises send many couples into financial panic.** In the world you will have tribulation. Things will break down. Unexpected bills will come. Furniture and car transmissions are not eternal. Often when a couple is hit with a financial crisis they call upon the credit card for help.

   Describe the most recent financial crisis you experienced:

   _____

   _____

   _____

   _____

Solution: You can prepare for a crisis. Set money aside for car repairs, home repairs, medical emergencies (including insurance deductibles), or a layoff from work. We replaced the transmission in our van recently, and because we had been setting aside $50 each month, we were able to write out a check for the repair, avoiding a financial crisis. Let me suggest a goal of six month's salary in savings to hedge against potential layoff. While we cannot anticipate every crisis, nor should we become so self-reliant we forsake dependency upon God, good planning for a potential crisis is wisdom.

Don't be too proud to ask your church family for help in a crisis. God has given us one another to meet those human needs.

9. **Failure to shop wisely will rob you.** Impulsive spending aside, sometimes we just don't shop smart. We pay more than we should, or we end up with something we don't use.

   Made any "dumb" purchases lately? _____

   _____

   _____

Solution: Be a smart shopper. When making a major purchase, take your time and do your homework. Consult a reliable financial publication such as *Consumer Reports*. Remember, cheapest is not always best. Measure your decision by more than just dollars and cents. Do not be afraid to buy secondhand. Generally, the greatest margin of profit is built into the purchase of an item when it is new.

10. **One of the greatest hindrances to financial freedom and stability is the failure to put God's will first.** Too often we make major purchases without seeking the counsel of God. Sometimes we make financial decisions that are in fact contrary to the will of God. I co-signed for a young man once (knowing that the Bible forbids co-signing) and it cost me dearly.

    Can you tell of a time you regretted a financial decision because of your failure to pray? _____

    _____

    _____

Solution: Seek first the kingdom of God and his righteousness. I heard a preacher say one time that he had baptized many men who testified to total surrender to Christ, but not one of them got baptized with his billfold in his pocket. Not that men should get their billfolds wet. What the preacher was saying was that too often he saw a failure to surrender totally to God when it comes to finances. It is not easy to surrender, but it is always best!

> *But seek first His kingdom and His righteousness; and all these things will be added to you.*
> — Matthew 6:33

Of the ten solutions suggested, how many are you currently practicing?

0   1   2   3   4   5   6   7   8   9   10

Which of the suggestions did you find most helpful?

_____

_____

_____

_____

Give And Live

The doorway to financial security and joy is found in giving. As a couple you will find great delight in faithfully fulfilling your commitment to Christ and his church — and to caring for the needs of those less fortunate.

The Bible has much to say about giving:

> *Give, and it will be given to you. They will pour into your lap a good measure — pressed down, shaken together and running over. For by your standard of measure it will be measured to you in return.*
> — Luke 6:38

Now this I say, he who sows sparingly will also reap sparingly, and he who sows bountifully will also reap bountifully. Each one must do just as he has purposed in his heart, not grudgingly or under compulsion, for God loves a cheerful giver.
— 2 Corinthians 9:6-7

When Elaine and I were church planters we conducted a city-wide survey, knocking on over 2,000 doors. We asked people why they thought folks who did not go to church did not go. The number two answer was, "Because the church is always asking for money!" It is a sad commentary on the church that there is a tremendous amount of fund-raisers, special offerings, or building funds that keep people inundated with requests. It is also tragic in our day that the average giving to the church is about one percent to three percent of our income, depending upon which survey you read.

A Word About Tithing

"Bring the whole tithe into the storehouse, so that there may be food in My house, and test Me now in this," says the LORD of hosts, "if I will not open for you the windows of heaven and pour out for you a blessing until it overflows."
— Malachi 3:10

What is tithing and is it intended for Christians today? The "tithe" is defined in *Ungers' Bible Dictionary*: **Tithe:** From the Greek word "dekate"; a tenth. In Mosaic Law the tenth of all produce, flocks and cattle was declared to be sacred to Jehovah.

When Malachi said, "Bring the whole tithe into the storehouse," he was speaking of ten percent of the first fruits of one's labor. The biblical percentage has not changed.

Jesus affirmed tithing in his statement to the Pharisees:

Woe to you, scribes and Pharisees, hypocrites! For you tithe mint and dill and cumin, and have neglected the weightier provisions of the law: justice and mercy and faithfulness; but these are the things you should have done without neglecting the others.
— Matthew 23:23

While Jesus gave a strong admonition regarding the Pharisees' neglect of justice, mercy, and faithfulness, he gave no provision for the neglect of the basics, such as tithing. Jesus does give a clear call to do whatever we do with a pure heart and a desire to honor God first.

Some seem to believe tithing ended with the New Covenant and grace. In a sense it did. Christians did not just give ten percent ... they gave all (Acts 2:45). We hear the excuse in our day, however, that "I don't have to tithe. We are under grace!" Grace is never an excuse to do less. It is always a call to more ... to a higher standard. Jesus did not come to do away with the law, but to fulfill it (Matthew 5:17). He takes us beyond the law. He challenges us to go the second mile, to give not only our coat, but our shirt also. Tithing is just a starting place in the joyous art of cheerful giving!

Giving is something we get to do, not what we've got to do. It comes from a grateful heart that has received much from a loving Father, God. Remember, the nature of God is to give. "For God so loved the world, He *gave*...." As those who have been created in his likeness and who are being conformed to the image of his Son, we too will be vessels of joyful generosity.

Cooling The Conflicts

Finances may be a significant stress in your marriage. I strongly urge you to begin now to apply the ten suggested solutions in this session. They really work.

With the realization that your situation may be intense currently, I further recommend you get financial counsel as soon as possible.

You can receive free financial counsel from a trained Christian counselor by contacting:
Crown Financial Ministries, Inc.
PO Box 100, Gainsville, GA 30503
1-800-722-1976
email: questions@crown.org

2 Peter 1:3 says, "His divine power has granted to us everything pertaining to life and godliness, through the true knowledge of Him who called us by His own glory and excellence." God has provided us with everything we need for every aspect of our lives if we will but look to him and his resources. You can see the financial turmoil turn to peace as you seek Godly counsel, and most of all, the help of the Lord himself.

Notes

The Reward Of Raising Children

Behold, children are a gift of the LORD, The fruit of the womb is a reward. Like arrows in the hand of a warrior, So are the children of one's youth.
— Psalm 127:3-4

In this Psalm attributed to Solomon, a powerful statement is made about children. They are a gift of God, a reward from him. They are compared to arrows that need set on the right course. Here are a few quotes about children I've heard from our culture.

"If this child had been our first, he would have been our last."

"Children are such a bother. We're not having any!"

"They're cute when they're babies, but when they get older, they are nothing but a pain!"

The fact that in America alone nearly 4,000 babies are aborted every day makes a clear statement that we don't see babies the way God does. Child abuse continues to increase, as well as abandonment. Have we scorned a gift from God? Have we allowed ourselves to become so deceived and calloused that we have come to see God's reward as repulsive?

The Devil's Got Us Duped

We read earlier about the fact that the devil goes after what God loves most. God loves marriage and the family. Both are a reflection of our relationship with him. We are not only his bride, we are his sons and daughters. Jesus said to call God, Father. Some of our greatest spiritual lessons about how God cares for us come to us as we care for our children.

Satan has saturated our culture with a message that has devalued children. Some have come to see children in purely a negative light! He has launched an all out attack on the family, undermining the very core values of our culture. It is time we take a stand and declare God's perspective on children and value the reward just as the Father does.

As we begin this session on the reward of raising children, please make every effort to look at children through the eyes of our heavenly Father. They are precious — a gift — a reward. God's intention is to bless us with children and enable us to be a blessing to our children.

To what degree do you see children as a gift — a reward?

0   1   2   3   4   5   6   7   8   9   10

67

Explain: _____
_____
_____
_____

Enough Reward Is Enough

Even in our decisions about childbearing (such as the number, the timing, and so forth), do we consider children to be a reward? I've never seen a person offered a reward, then turn it down saying something like, "Oh no, I just can't handle a reward right now." Most people I know willingly, graciously, and enthusiastically welcome gifts and rewards. Is that how we welcome children? Are we perhaps quick to cut off the flow of reward from God by determining we want no more children?

> *Elaine and I had three children — two girls and one boy. We decided our quiver was full. Our energy levels, our income, and our circumstances brought us to the very clear conclusion that we were done with childbearing. Late one evening while driving home I was listening to* Focus on the Family. *They were interviewing couples with large families (eight to thirteen children). I listened in amazement. One father said, "What troubles me is how many Christians who never pray about the decision of childbearing — are those who prevent children for the very same reasons most abortions are done." The Holy Spirit whispered, "Are you listening?" I began to weep. When I got home, I knew Elaine and I must talk. When we sat down to talk I discovered God had been telling her the same thing. We asked God's forgiveness for our failure to seek his counsel. Our precious daughter, Kay, is a result of that prayer. Not only did we have our family enlarged, but our hearts were enlarged to see children, not as a burden, but as a blessing.*

Tell about how prayer has been a part of your childbearing decisions: _____
_____
_____
_____
_____

There is not a right or wrong *number* of children to have, but there is a right and a wrong *attitude* to have. With gratitude, embrace the reward(s) from God, open to all of the gift(s) he has in store for you.

Invest In The Treasure

Children are a treasure! Because children are a gift from God, they are a precious and priceless investment. We can pour ourselves into our work, our home, or even our church, but what we pour into our children will render the greatest fruit. Do not underestimate the value of the time you invest in the lives of your children.

Here are a few investment tips ...

1. **Love each other first.** Don't allow your marriage to become "child" centered. A couple can fall into the trap of investing the vast majority of their attention and affections into their children. Your relationship as husband and wife is primary. The best gift you can give your children is to be and stay deeply in love and committed to each other. Children who know their parents love and respect each other are secure, content, and even better behaved.

   To what degree is your relationship child-centered? (10 equals most)

   0   1   2   3   4   5   6   7   8   9   10

   Explain: _____

   _____

   _____

   Is it evident to your children you and your spouse love one another and are committed to each other?

   ___ yes   ___ no   ___ not sure

   Explain: _____

   _____

   _____

2. **Be real.** Children are experts at discerning phoniness! "Do as I say not as I do" is garbage! Your example speaks louder than any words you will ever say. You will mess up from time to time. Admit it when you do. Being willing to admit your own faults will set an example for your children of how to deal with mistakes ... and even sin.

   I was really tired one night after a long day of counseling. Elaine was off to a women's meeting and I was home with all four children, ages eight, six, four, and one. I don't remember what Ben did, but I remember I allowed it to make me very angry. I raised my voice and it frightened him. Later after I had regained my composure I said, "Daddy really blew it, didn't he? I shouldn't have yelled at you, son." He agreed with me. I asked his forgiveness. Ben had done something wrong and he deserved discipline, but he did not deserve unkind words with harsh, loud tones. Ben and I both remember that night — but as a night when Dad was big enough to admit he was wrong and ask forgiveness.

   Being real is what integrity is. Practice what you preach with your children. (How many times had I told Ben not to yell at his sisters?) If there are things you don't want your children doing or saying, then you must make every effort to model those things.

   Bill and Ruth kept telling Michael just how important Sunday school and church were. It was so important that one of them would get up each Sunday morning and get Michael ready so they could drop him off at the church up the street. Bill and

69

Ruth didn't attend Sunday school ever, and worship service rarely. Bill's mom made him go when he was a boy so he refused to go now! Ruth used Sunday to catch up around the house. They couldn't understand that as Michael got older he began to rebel against there insistence on his church involvement.

Is there something in your life you absolutely would not want your child to do (as a child or as an adult), yet you are doing it yourself right now? ___ yes ___ no

Can you talk about what it is? _____

_____

_____

3. **Sharpen those arrows.** Parents have a responsibility to "train up a child in the way he/she should go" (Proverbs 22:6). Sharpen those arrows God has given you and point them in the right direction. Instruct them in the Word of God. While all of the teaching and training of your children is not directly up to you to do, you are *responsible* for all of it. Are you fully aware of what your children are being taught in school? Are you certain your children are receiving solid, biblical education from the church fellowship in which you are involved? How much time do you invest in your children, instructing them in Christian principles? If you want your children to have fruitful lives, make training them up in righteousness a priority.

Tell about how you are involved in the spiritual training of your child/children:

_____

_____

_____

4. **Dare to discipline with courage.** A woman was fleeing with her crying three-year-old from Wal-Mart. As she made her dash to the car I heard her exclaim, "I just can't make her mind." Already that child was in control. Proverbs 23:13 says, "Do not hold back discipline from the child, although you strike him with the rod, he will not die." Do not be afraid to discipline your child. If you struggle with the fear of disciplining your children, or wonder when and how to discipline, I strongly recommend James Dobson's excellent book, *Dare to Discipline*. Proverbs 23:14 says, "You shall strike him with the rod and rescue his soul from Sheol." Scriptures clearly teach that firm discipline is necessary to keep your child on the right course.

Caution
While I do believe the scriptures do encourage corporal punishment such as spanking, I do not believe the Bible condones ever bringing actual physical harm to the child. Physical abuse is never tolerated or encouraged. Never spank when you are angry. There is too much risk that you will exceed proper limitations.

Describe your typical disciplinary actions that you employ with your child or children: _____
_____
_____
_____

5. **Discipline in unity.** If the two of you are not in unity when it comes to the disciplining of your children, they will be confused and frustrated. They will quickly learn to "play" you against each other. Take the time to talk and come to agreement on how and when you will discipline. Often in a marriage one parent is permissive and the other is strict. Find a middle ground (which is actually probably best) and be *consistent* in your discipline.

   To what degree are you in unity in regards to how and when to discipline? (10 is best)

   0   1   2   3   4   5   6   7   8   9   10

   Explain: _____
   _____
   _____
   _____

6. **Discipline with instruction.** "A wise son (daughter) accepts his (her) father's discipline" (Proverbs 13:1). In the King James Version of the Bible it says "instruction" instead of discipline. Discipline is instruction. The word "disciple," which is the root word of discipline, means a learner. Every time your children receive correction they need to be given direction. Disciplining a child is an opportune teaching moment. Even with very small children, a word about "why" he or she is being disciplined is appropriate. Avoid saying, "Because I told you!" When a child asks why he or she is being corrected, tell them why.

   Do you talk with your child when you give disciplinary correction?

   ____ yes   ____ no   ____ some

   Explain: _____
   _____
   _____
   _____

7. **Apply authority appropriately.** I am convinced that parents should never need to yell or become red faced. Parents have lost sight of their God-given authority when they resort to emotional demonstrations of power. I heard an illustration on *Focus on the Family* (Yes, I listen to them a lot!), once about a police officer pulling someone over for an offense. The officer does not yell, get red faced, or call you names. He or she calmly, quietly walks up to your window and ask for your driver's license. They are calm because they understand their authority — and that what they are about to do is for your good — and for the good of others.

   Keep your cool when it comes to correcting your child. It is your responsibility and your God-given authority to exercise discipline.

100 degrees
90 degrees
80 degrees
70 degrees
60 degrees
50 degrees
40 degrees

To what degree do you get "hot" when it comes to correcting your children? (Use a red pen and fill in the thermometer to represent your emotional level.)

Explain: _____
_____
_____
_____
_____
_____
_____
_____
_____
_____

8. **Bring on the affirmation.** Your child needs seven words of encouragement for every word of correction. Do you compliment and build up your child? Avoid using name-calling or words that demean. When you affirm your child, look for opportunities to speak about character, not just behavior or appearance. Rather than saying, "That was a nice thing to do," say "that was very kind." "You certainly were generous with your toys, Sally." In doing so, you build into the character of your child more than outward appearances or behaviors.

    List at least five qualities you can affirm about your child/children:

    _____
    _____
    _____
    _____
    _____

9. **Love your children.** Build a deep love relationship with your child. Spend quantity and quality time with your children. Be involved in their lives and be aware of what's going on with them. Love them by keeping your promises.

    If you fail to keep a commitment, admit it and ask forgiveness. Josh McDowell said recently at a Promise Keepers event that "rules without relationship foster rebellion." When your children know they are loved, they better understand that rules are signals of love, that protect and nurture them.

    To what degree are you confident your children know you love them? (Place the initials of each child by the appropriate number.) 10 is most confident.

    0   1   2   3   4   5   6   7   8   9   10

Explain: _____
_____
_____

10. **Introduce your child to Jesus.** The greatest investment you can make in this gift from God is to point your children to Jesus. Introducing your child to Jesus is an eternal investment. Don't wait for someone else to share Christ with your son or daughter. At a very early age, sow seeds of God's love into the heart of your child. Pray with your children each night as you tuck them into bed. Do not assume that because you have been a Christian example that your child has come to a personal saving knowledge of Christ. Present God's plan of salvation clearly to your child.

    If you are unsure how to present the plan of salvation to your child, contact your pastor or a local Christian bookstore for suggested resources.

    As your children grow, it is good to regularly ask them how they are doing in their relationship with Christ. Especially with children who received Christ at a very early age, it is good to revisit their commitment.

    A resource available to assist you in leading your children to Christ — and to training them with a solid biblical foundation is *The Inheritance*. It is a one-year Christian mentoring course designed for children ages nine to fourteen.

    Have you introduced your child/children to Jesus Christ?

    ___ yes   ___ no   ___ sort of

    Explain: _____
    _____
    _____

You've Only Just Begun

Parenting is an ongoing adventure. There are many great resources out there to help you.

• Be involved in a Christ-centered, biblically grounded church that is family oriented.

• Seek opportunities to enhance your parenting skills: seminars, books, Christian radio/television programs.

• Don't be afraid to ask for help. Call your pastor, mentor, or counselor when you need advice.

• Pray regularly for wisdom and help from the one who wants the very best for your family.

Notes

Intimacy In Every Way

... and they shall become one flesh. And the man and his wife were both naked and were not ashamed.   — Genesis 2:24b-25

Webster defines "intimacy" this way: "Marked by very close association, contact or familiarity."

A friend shared with me that the word "intimacy" could be defined when you sound it out like this, in-to-me-see. Intimacy then is a transparent love relationship of acceptance, commitment, and care.

In spite of what many men and women think, intimacy and sex are not synonymous. How often have you heard your spouse say, "Do you want to be intimate tonight?" Intimacy transcends sexual intercourse. In fact, intimacy is the avenue to the ultimate satisfaction in sexual intercourse.

How intimate are you and your spouse? (10 is very intimate)

| 0 | 1 | 2 | 3 | 4 | 5 | 6 | 7 | 8 | 9 | 10 |

Explain: _____
_____
_____
_____

Nothing Hidden

Are you comfortable being totally naked with your spouse? (Aren't you glad that's not a fill in the blank question?) Many would respond that they are embarrassed to be naked even with their spouse. Some think they are not pretty or they don't want their spouse to see physical flaws. Others think being naked together is "dirty." Adam and Eve were naked and unashamed. I believe they were naked (or transparent) not only physically, but relationally, emotionally, spiritually, and in every other way. Adam and Eve walked in pure intimacy until The Fall.

The Result Of The Fall

Unresolved sin leaves stain that we scurry to cover. Adam and Eve ran to hide, not only from God, but they sought to cover their nakedness from each other. Rather than dealing with their sin, they tried to cover it up.

Unresolved past sins, or present ones will result in a blockade to intimacy. Consider the following:

- Unforgiveness of past hurts will spill over into your present relationships. Resolve in your heart to forgive.

- Unresolved immoral sexual sin will taint your own sexual relationship and the overall intimacy of your marriage. I encourage you to abide by 1 John 1:9 / James 5:16 and to confess that sin of perversion, pre-marital sex, or any other sexual sin and walk through the steps of forgiveness with a trusted Christian friend or counselor. Don't cover it up!

- Emotional or sexual abuse prior to your marriage needs resolution. Far too many people were abused by a parent, sibling, close relative, or friend and never told anyone, never dealt with it, and it continues to hinder current intimacy. Talk with your spouse, pastor, or Christian counselor if you sense there is work needed in this area.

- Repent of any sin currently hindering intimacy in your marriage. Your love for work or material things more than your spouse is sin. Hours on the computer or at sports events will prevent true intimacy in your marriage. Addiction to pornography or having given your "heart" to another other than your spouse, is sin. There is an adultery of the heart that both women and men commit that is equally as destructive as physical adultery. Confess it as sin and repent.

Don't cover up any sin that puts a stain on your intimacy. Be quick to deal with it rightly. Allow God to come in, cleanse and restore.

Pause And Ponder

Ask the Holy Spirit to expose in your heart any sin you have tried to cover up. Confess it to God right now. Ask him to forgive and cleanse you. You still may need to share this with your spouse, pastor, counselor, or friend.

With The Fall Came A Prideful Wall

Pride erected a huge barrier between Adam and Eve, and it will between you and your spouse. Did you notice that after Adam and Eve sinned they scurried to find fig leaves? They sewed them together and covered *themselves*. Adam was not trying to cover Eve — nor Eve cover Adam. They were frantic to cover themselves.

Self-centered pride prompts us to maintain this armor shield so others cannot see what is really inside. Remember intimacy is in-to-me-see. The truth is there is stuff we don't want even our spouse to see. Weaknesses, inner thoughts, even physical blemishes are protected by our pride.

God loves humility. He is opposed to the proud (1 Peter 5:5). Do you want to be in a place of opposition with God?

I'm not a kid anymore. My once slim and trim physic has given way to skin tags, flab, and even a few wrinkles. (Just a few.) Recently I had a bout with bloat. My stomach would stick out like a pregnant woman. (In fact, my youngest child asked me if I was pregnant.) I did everything I could to avoid having Elaine see my expanded middle. I found bigger T-shirts to sleep in at night. Gently the Holy Spirit brought me back to Genesis, exposed my pride and I asked forgiveness. I was allowing my preoccupation with self and senseless pride to hinder our intimacy.

Pride keeps us from asking each other for help — or for prayers. It keeps us from being open to God's ordained purposes of ministry to one another.

Has pride been a hindrance to intimacy in your marriage?   ___ yes   ___ no   ___ some

Explain: _____
_____
_____

Fear Follows Close To Pride And Frustrates Intimacy

It is clear that as Adam and Eve were crouching in the bushes they were afraid. They were afraid of facing the consequences of their sin. They feared rejection and retaliation. At least part of what causes us to cover ourselves is the fear that we will be rejected by our spouse. We may fear that if we expose some vulnerability the consequences will be more than we can bear.

There may be necessary, painful consequences for some darkness in your life that needs exposed. For example, if a spouse must admit to an extra-marital affair, the road to restoration will be a process with tears and difficult decisions. True repentance is often difficult. Let me assure you that the opportunity to see intimacy restored is worth the investment of dealing with the consequences of your sin. You cannot cover it up forever. Besides, the ultimate consequences will be even more costly if you continue to cover your sin.

It may not be a sin, however, that you are harboring. It may just be weakness, and fear has convinced you that if you admit that weakness — if you allow your spouse to see-into-you, he or she will reject you. Perhaps you need to talk with a trusted Christian friend, pastor, mentor, or counselor prior to talking with your spouse to secure spiritual advice on how to remove the "fig leaves" that hinder the intimacy in your marriage.

List other hindrances to intimacy that you have observed or experienced:
_____
_____
_____
_____
_____
_____

The ramifications of The Fall in the Garden, and our own failure to confront our own sins and weaknesses are numerous and complex. The good news is that the cleansing blood of Christ makes all things new. The God of restoration has dealt with the curse of The Fall and has enabled us to find our way back to Eden.

Let me say again, marriage is to be the most life-giving human relationship you will experience on the planet. As you guard and nurture intimacy in your marriage you will find the greatest delight and fruitfulness in your union.

Sex And Intimacy

While intimacy is not sexual intercourse, sexual intercourse is intended to be one of the greatest expressions of intimacy. A man and a woman, totally vulnerable, give themselves to one another in a mutual act of love and physical delight. Sex was God's idea. If you haven't noticed, he did an awesome job designing our bodies for ultimate pleasure.

The Bible gives some solid ground rules for sexual activity between a husband and wife. Abiding by God's design not only assures the ultimate in intimacy, but the very best of physical delight.

Principle #1: Your Body Is Not Your Own

> *The husband must fulfill his duty to his wife, and likewise also the wife to her husband. The wife does not have authority over her own body, but the husband does; and likewise also the husband does not have authority over his own body, but the wife does.* — 1 Corinthians 7:3-4

It was a popular sitcom, but it was a scene you could have seen in many sitcoms — or in too many homes. The couple has had an argument. The wife stomps into the bedroom grabs a pillow and blanket, throws them in her husband's face and says, "You're sleeping on the couch." In other words, until this matter is settled to the wife's satisfaction, there will be no sexual relations.

Sex is abused and misused in many marriages. It is a beautiful gift of God to be mutually shared and enjoyed throughout your lifetime. God's Word has some very practical things to say about your sexual relationship.

The biblical view of the physical relationship between a man and woman is one of "my body is not mine, it is his, or hers." You will belong to each other. Therefore you have relinquished personal rights in good faith, trust, love, and devotion to each other.

What does it mean to relinquish rights? First of all, it by no means gives way to an abusive situation. It means both of you have hearts set on pleasing your spouse physically, never *using* sex to punish or control the other. The key to the success of this biblical picture is that both of you understand the concept. Paul is telling us that the sexual relationship is *not* fifty percent-fifty percent — it is *not* give and take. It is one hundred percent give from *both* of you, then you will find great delight.

What do the verses from 1 Corinthians 7 say to you?

_____

_____

_____

_____

Principle #2: Mutual Consent Is God's Design

Before you begin to think that giving yourself fully to your spouse must mean you must have sex at any time or place he or she demands, we must read on to verse 5 of 1 Corinthians 7, "Stop depriving one another, except by agreement for a time that you may devote yourselves to prayer, and come together again lest Satan tempt you because of your lack of self-control."

The overall concept of scripture of the sexual relationship is one of mutuality. Because you both have fully, mutually relinquished your rights to the other, you are in a relationship of giving yourself to your spouse. Out of that mutual love and sharing, there are also times you will agree together to abstain from sexual intercourse.

Two biblical principles are clear from Paul's words:

a. **Abstaining needs to be done with agreement.** The foundational truth to remember here is that _the decision to have or to not have sex should never be made by one member of the relationship alone._ It should always be a mutual decision.

Paul speaks of prayer as one reason for mutually abstaining. There are, however, other legitimate reasons for the couple to agree to refrain from sexual intercourse. Sickness, late term pregnancy, fatigue, stress, conflict, all can be justifiable reasons to abstain. The important matter is to talk — and come to a place of mutual agreement.

Why is mutual agreement so important when it comes to the decision to refrain from sexual intercourse? _____

_____

_____

b. **It is not good to abstain too long.** Paul warns not to stay apart too long, or you will give the devil an opportunity to tempt you. Don't be fooled by the cunning enemy, thinking you can go for long periods of time without sexual relations. Even though it may not lead to unfaithfulness, it will diminish the richness of your union and allow the enemy, and your flesh, to direct your thought-life into forbidden territory.

Principle #3: Understanding Leads To Delight

In Session 6 we talked about differences. When it comes to sexual activity, men and women are very different. Through dialogue (and perhaps some study) it is valuable to understand those differences and grow with them. Strive to understand how the two of you differ regarding sex. Here are some helpful hints to remember.

a. **Men and women view sex differently.** When asked why they participated in sexual intercourse before marriage, men answered, "Because I love *it*." Women answered, "Because I love *him*." Among men, *Playboy* is the number-one best seller. Women hold *Better Homes and Gardens* as their favorite. Men tend to view sex as an event or activity, while women see sex as a relational experience of intimacy.

b. **Men and women approach sex differently.** Someone once said that when it comes to sex, women are like crock-pots, and men are like microwave ovens. Men, being primarily visually stimulated, tend to be ready for sexual intercourse quickly while women are still thinking about the book they had been reading. A woman needs her husband to take his time, and to assure her that his love is for *her*, not for sex.

c. **Men and women conclude sex differently.** Microwaves not only heat up quickly, they finish the job fast as well. Often after climax, a man is ready to roll over and go to sleep. The woman is still very much sexually and *emotionally* energized. She is delighted with caressing and kisses even after climax.

As you both are sensitive to these differences and communicate with one another, you will see your sex-life get more precious with each passing day of marriage. Understanding these differences will enhance your sexual intimacy.

What are some other differences you can think of in how men and women approach sexual activity? _____
_____
_____
_____
_____

Principle #4: Communication Is Crucial For Sexual Fulfillment

The fact that Paul encourages agreement on sexual restraint implies dialogue about sex. Be willing to discuss sexual matters with your spouse. Sex is not a forbidden topic and discussion about sexual intercourse will not diminish the satisfaction you both will find; it will enhance it.

> *Chuck and Mary remained married for less than two years. Their sexual relationship had never been fulfilling. Unknown to Chuck, sexual intercourse was very painful for Mary, and because of that she avoided sex, coming up with excuses to refrain. Chuck experienced constant rejection and hurt. He tried to get Mary to talk about their sexual problems, even encouraging seeking counsel. Mary grew up with*

the conviction that sex was a forbidden topic of discussion. She refused to discuss or seek counsel for their problems. A few months after their divorce, Mary learned she had a birth defect that restricted her sexual activity, making intercourse difficult and painful. Sadly, too late she learned a truth that could have brought help to their marriage. Her unwillingness to talk or seek counsel led to the end of their marriage.

Always be willing to discuss sexual matters. There are a few questions I encourage couples to discuss often:

Ask your spouse if there is anything in your sexual activity that makes them uncomfortable or feel demeaned. Listen non-defensively to their reply.

Talk about ways to improve your sexual relationship. Ask your spouse if there are things you can do to make the sexual encounter more meaningful.

Be certain that emotionally you are in a good place before the physical begins. Ask if there is some offense, hurt, or anger that is unresolved.

Communicate your love and devotion to one another daily, throughout the day. Speak words of encouragement and praise to your spouse that genuinely communicates your love for him or her as a person.

To what degree do you feel comfortable to talk about sex with your spouse?

0	1	2	3	4	5	6	7	8	9	10
Not at all					Mostly					Very

Explain: _____
_____
_____

Principle #5: Keep The Marriage Bed Pure

Paul wrote to the Corinthians, "For you have been bought with a price; therefore glorify God in your body" (1 Corinthians 6:20). Remember that your body — your sexual relationship — your whole marriage belongs to God and is to be an avenue for God to be glorified.

The author of Hebrews wrote, "Let marriage be held in honor among all, and let the marriage bed be undefiled; for fornicators and adulterers God will judge" (Hebrews 13:4).

Keep your relationship pure in the sight of God and each other. Stay absolutely faithful to your spouse, not looking to the left or to the right with desire for another.

Avoid pornographic materials. Find your sexual stimulation only in your spouse. It is an offense to your wife or husband that you require looking upon another woman or man to find sexual satisfaction.

Avoid sexual jokes that demean God's gift of sex and make sexual intercourse out to be something dirty or obscene.

Guard the privacy of your bedroom. If you are having problems in your sexual relationship, don't make it a matter of public information. (Don't even tell your prayer group.) If you need counsel, seek confidential Christian counsel.

Can you think of other attitudes or activities that might defile your marriage bed?

_____
_____
_____
_____

Your sexual relationship is a wonderful gift from God. Work together to make it more precious all of your days together on planet earth.

> *An excellent resource on the topic of sexual fulfillment is Dr. Ed Wheat's book,* Intended for Pleasure.

Notes

Fueling The Flames Of Your Marriage

It is recommended that Session 10 be completed during a getaway weekend. If this is *not* possible, do the game, video, vow renewal, overview, and closing prayer.

Session 10 Schedule
Evening Session
Candlelight Dinner
The Flame Game
Break Period
Worship Songs
    "That's Why We Praise Him"
    "Meet Us"
Prayer
A Vow To Cherish Video Presentation
Break Period
Vow Renewal
Private Time Assignment
Closing Prayer

Morning Session
Breakfast
Worship Songs
    "Open The Eyes Of My Heart, Lord"
    "Draw Me Close To You"
Session 10 Overview
Break Period
Small Group Time
Return For Closing Prayer
    (The Lord's Supper may be offered before the prayer)

Fueling The Flames Of Your Marriage

Drink water from your own cistern And fresh water from your own well. Should your springs be dispersed abroad, Streams of water in the streets? Let them be yours alone And not for strangers with you. Let your fountain be blessed, And rejoice in the wife of your youth. As a loving hind and a graceful doe, Let her breasts satisfy you at all times; Be exhilarated always with her love.

— Proverbs 5:15-19

Several years ago we took a group from our church on a float trip, canoeing down the Piney River. One evening as we were seated around the campfire singing and fellowshiping, I noticed something remarkable about our fire. A few of the logs had rolled apart as the fire burned, and many of the ends of logs no longer touched. The fire was burning low and on its way to extinguishing. While there was plenty of wood for a roaring blaze, because the fire had been unattended and had gotten scattered, it was going out. One of the men of our group jumped up and with a stick began to rearrange the burning logs so they were in tight together again. Soon we all had to scoot back from the roaring flames.

Marriages are like campfires. They need attention. You and your spouse must stay close for the flames to burn warm and bright. Too many marriages have been allowed to grow cold and dark. God's intentions for you is a lifelong relationship of life-giving light and warmth.

Rate the flames of your marital fire. (10 is really hot!)

0	1	2	3	4	5	6	7	8	9	10
Soot only		Embers		Flickering flames			Burning blaze			Red hot

Explain: _____
_____
_____

So there is no confusion, when I write about the "flames" of your marriage, I am not speaking only of passion or sexual satisfaction. A marriage ablaze with life is full of commitment, communication, care, respect, as well as a deep sense of abiding love. The fire is well rounded, tightly woven, steady, and warm.

Extinguishers Of Endearment

On our little canoe trip, the fire suffered primarily because of neglect. Often neglect is the main cause of the demise of the flames of a marriage, but sometimes there are extinguishers that come in like a huge bucket of water. Let's take a look at some forces that can cause your marriage to smolder and grow cold.

1. **We're Just Busy!** We have four children, all active and involved in life. We are in the season as a family where there is a lot going on — piano, violin, football, school functions, as well as church activities. Our mini-van is constantly on the move. It takes a conscious, willful effort to keep communication channels strong and the bonds of love secure when things are hectic.

   To what degree is busyness a flame retardant in your marriage?

   0   1   2   3   4   5   6   7   8   9   10

   Explain: _____

   _____

   _____

2. **Taking For Granted.** In the many years that I've been counseling couples, repeatedly I hear the words, "He (or she) just takes me for granted." One wife told me she felt like she was on about the same value level as a piece of the furniture. It's unfortunate that after good years of loving commitment, a couple can fall in the destructive attitude of apathy — taking one another for granted. Sadly, often one takes the other for granted, while one works hard to keep the flames alive.

   Have you ever felt like your spouse takes you for granted?

   ___ yes   ___ no   ___ some

   Explain: _____

   _____

   _____

3. **Two Different Worlds.** He has his friends; she has hers. She goes to her job; he goes to his. She goes to church on Sunday; he goes fishing. He watches football; she watches figure skating. As interests roll apart (like the logs in a fire), the flames grow dim and cold. Conversations become difficult because there is so little common ground. The attractions that distract us from one another in a marriage today are not only more numerous, but more intense.

   On an average, how many hours weekly do you spend together participating in the same thing? (This can include playing with your children together, but do not count sleeping!

   2   4   6   8   10   12   14   16   18   20   more

   Explain: _____

   _____

   _____

4. **Don't Stuff Stuff.** Sarah had been a good and faithful wife for over 25 years. She had never crossed Harold, striving to be a submissive wife. She responded to his ridicule and insults with a pleasant smile, never once returning his hurtful words with her own. Then one day Sarah had had enough. When Harold drove in from work, he knew something was up. He found suitcases on the front porch. Sarah was on her way out. Harold was totally clueless that Sarah was dissatisfied with him or their marriage.

While I commend Sarah for striving to be a peacemaker, and I acknowledge that Harold was a dead-beat husband, I believe this marriage could have been salvaged and restored to a life-giving glow if Sarah had not been such a "stuffer" of all that was coming her way. Most "blow-ups" that happen in a marriage could be avoided if each little burst of wind into the fragile bubble had been dealt with as it came. When there is an explosive argument that can snuff out the life of a marriage, very rarely is just one issue the problem. Stuff that has been building all comes to a head at once, and spills out over the flames of the marriage.

Tell about something you "stuffed" and it did not come out until much later that it really had disturbed you:

_____
_____
_____
_____
_____
_____
_____

How could you have handled the situation more positively? _____

_____
_____
_____
_____

5. **Words That Wound.** While some people "stuff" too much, others "spout" too much. Without thinking, hurtful, degrading words spill out like a flood and extinguish the flames.

A very subtle "fire extinguisher" I have seen has been teasing.

> *Hank was a funny guy, always quick to tell a joke or get in a tease. His wife, Sally, was often the focus of his jokes. He would publicly talk about what a "dumb blonde" Sally was. He could say "one-liners" that would cut to the quick, wounding Sally deeply. A caring friend who loved both Hank and Sally confronted Hank about his comments. Hank was quick to say, "Hey, I'm only teasing! Sally knows that! I always make fun of people I love the most! Right, Sally?" Sally sheepishly agreed, but it was evident that inwardly her pain was deep.*

Words can wound — and the wounds can drive a wedge that causes the blaze of your marriage to lose its brilliance.

Have hurtful words been a hindrance in your marriage?

___ yes   ___ no   ___ some

Explain: _____

_____

_____

6. **Refusal To Forgive.** Nothing kills the fires of a marriage quicker and more completely than the failure to forgive. Hebrews 12:15 says, "See to it that no one comes short of the grace of God; that no root of bitterness springing up causes trouble, and by it many be defiled." A root of bitterness in a marriage is destructive. It is like a cancer that eats away at the very fabric of your union, drawing the life out of both of you. Be always ready to forgive fully.

Often a hindrance to forgiveness is the inability to admit you have wronged your spouse. We need to speak the words, "I was wrong. Will you please forgive me?"

Forgiveness does not mean we forget the offense. When the prophet Jeremiah heard the Lord say, "I will forgive their iniquity, and their sin I will remember no more" (Jeremiah 31:34), Jeremiah knew God would not actually forget the sin. God knows everything. He has perfect memory. God meant he would no longer hold that sin against them. It would be as a debt that had been paid in full — or cancelled.

When you forgive one another, you must forget the offense insofar as that you no longer hold it against the other. Practically what that means is when you have an argument, you don't dig up something that happened years ago — or even recently that has been forgiven.

To what degree are you guilty of continuing to bring up past failures to your spouse?

0   1   2   3   4   5   6   7   8   9   10

Explain: _____

_____

_____

7. **No Counsel Allowed!** I am convinced that any conflict can be resolved with prayer and dialogue. I have seen the fires of too many marriages extinguished by the absolute refusal to seek counsel and work through issues. There is no cause for shame to admit you need outside help to find renewal in your marriage. Proverbs 13:10b says, "With those who receive counsel is wisdom."

I want to ask you to make a pledge to one another. Be willing to seek counsel upon the request of either of you in the marriage. I have found that even though I may not think there is a problem, or I may think it can be resolved by just the two of us, that my willingness to sensitively respond to the request of my spouse to seek counsel is already a step toward healing. Don't make excuses and don't put it off. Seek godly counsel.

> **If at any time your spouse feels the need to seek counsel, feeling there is a breakdown of communication, resolve and pledge right now that you will be willing to participate.**
>
> ____ **I pledge to be willing to seek counsel at any time my spouse feels it is necessary.**
>
> **Signed:** _____

Seven Suggestions To Keep The Flames Burning

1. **Participate in "creative" dating.** On a regular basis (no less than once a month) have a creative date together. By creative, I mean you should not just go to a movie or concert. Do something that allows you to communicate while you are together. If you do go to a movie, include dinner together — or a walk in the park. Elaine and I like miniature golf (although she always wins).

    Creative dates can be very inexpensive. You can trade-off babysitting with other couples. You can just go out for a cup of coffee, take a bike ride, or enjoy a casual drive.

    If you have trouble getting good conversation going, I recommend the Focus on the Family publication, *Creative Conversation Starters for Couples*, by the Crosbys.

    Tell about your most recent date as a couple: _____
    _____
    _____
    _____
    _____

2. **Overnight getaways are a must!** It's a little tricky for us with four children to get away for an overnight. (The last time we had an overnight, we shipped the children out to friends and stayed home together.) Consistently take time away from your children, other family members, and friends and have an overnight retreat. (I recommend no less than once every two months.)

    Overnights can be work and play. Elaine and I often spend part of our time away "catching up" on calendar issues. A few times we have done budget review and revision. Some of our overnight retreats have been for the purpose of prayer. Regardless of the focus of each of those getaways, each has been rewarding and has fueled the flames of our marriage.

How often do you and your spouse get away alone for an overnight time together? (Circle number that reflects per year.)

  1   2   3   4   5   6   7   8   9   10   11   12   more

Discuss: _____
_____
_____

3. **Keep "courting" one another.**

> *I noticed that Bill and Thelma had something most couples do not have. Love and respect was evident in how they spoke to one another — and even how they touched. When the opportunity arose to go to a workshop on marriage they were teaching, I signed up first. They spoke of the commitment to consistently express appreciation and adoration for one another. For years in a fruitful, deep relationship of love, they had continued to court one another.*

Let me suggest three ways you can court your spouse and keep the fires burning.

Appreciation: Say thank you a lot. Tell them specific things for which you give thanks. Tell others of your gratitude for your spouse.

Affection: A hug, a kiss, or a note on the mirror are all simple ways to say, "I love you." (Thelma would put a "dab" of her perfume on Bill's pillow when he would come to our men's retreats.)

Adoration: Always show honor and respect. Open the door for her. Praise him to others for a job well done.

List some ways you can express love and appreciation for your spouse:

_____
_____
_____
_____
_____
_____

4. **Laugh a lot together!** Many have commented there is a lot of laughter in the Donovan home. I must tell you that it is because the joy of the Lord is our strength. Jesus has given us joy and gladness.

There is, however, a conscious effort to allow humor to creep in on a regular basis in our home. Funny stuff happens every day. I heard someone say, "Man is most humorous when he takes himself too seriously." Even in serious moments, we can discover cause for a smile.

I was praying with Ben one night. He had had a rough day. Not only that, his room was a wreck. He had spilled his fish food so his room had a strong odor of something like "stink bait." After listing all his problems, we began to pray. I began, "Dear God, Ben needs help!" I paused, opened one eye just as Ben opened one eye and we both began to chuckle. I know that on the surface there isn't much funny about that scene, but at that very moment my son and I seized an opportunity to laugh together. I think God chuckled, too.

Elaine and I do the same thing. Almost daily as a couple, we discover rich opportunities for laughter. Our laughter is *never* at the expense of another. We strive always to laugh *with* one another, never *at* one another. We *never* implement *coarse* jesting. We work hard to avoid sarcastic teasing. (That is not "fun" humor.)

Tell about something funny that happened recently between you and your spouse:

_____
_____
_____
_____

5. **Participate in a Marriage Enrichment course or event.** (You already are on the right road.) I recommend that annually (or no less than once every two years), a couple invest time and money in a biblically based marriage enrichment opportunity.

There is so much help out there for our marriages. Couples have no excuse for failure. Keep your marriage a priority, looking for every opportunity to make it stronger.

Before this course, what marriage enrichment opportunity had you experienced?

_____
_____

What did you find most helpful? _____

_____
_____
_____
_____

What have you found helpful about this course? _____

_____
_____
_____
_____

6. **Look for common ground.** A marriage really stands on what happens day in and day out. The special events and enrichment emphasis are crucial, but what you do with what you've learned when you face Monday together is what matters most.

Be sure your days are filled with some common activities with your spouse. Do your shopping together from time to time. Be involved in commitments that cause you to spend time with each other, not apart. Pick up the phone and call during the day just to "check in" and say, "I love you."

When you have to be apart for work or travel, assure your spouse that your thoughts are often of him or her.

Even with children and all of their activities, work hard to share those opportunities together. Let me encourage you to not overload your children (and family) with too many extra-curricular activities. If you find yourself running frantically with the schedules pulling you apart rather than together, sit down and re-evaluate the schedules.

List several common activities you can share together: _____
_____
_____
_____
_____

7. **Grow spiritually together and the fires will burn bright.**

> *It was really a surprise to Dustin and Sherry that a twelve-week course in the fundamentals of Christianity would renew their marriage. As they watched the videos on the basics of Christianity, unknown to them, God was bringing them closer as one in Christ. When they discovered the reality of the person of the Holy Spirit, they also discovered a new depth of love for one another.*

Since Christ is the head of your marriage, as you draw closer to him, your relationship will become more like he intends it to be. It will truly be life-giving for both of you.

To keep the marriage fires burning, intentionally seize opportunities to grow spiritually together. Attend church service together. Participate in special renewal events together. You may want to experience a short-term foreign mission trip as a couple.

Pray together. Pray out loud for one another, giving thanks for your spouse. Pray for specific needs. I always encourage men as priest over the home to lead in the area of prayer, but either of you can initiate a time to join hands and pray.

Describe how you have grown together spiritually as a couple and how that has affected your marriage: _____

_____

_____

_____

_____

In Conclusion

God's will is for your marriage to just get "better-n-better"! Because he is at work in you, you can count on his nature to be increasing in your relationship. God loves marriage — and he loves you. Stay on course on the wonderful journey of joy as a couple.

Resources For Further Study And Growth

The Bait of Satan, John Bevere, Creation House

Becoming the Parent God Wants You to Be, Kevin Leman, NavPress

Transforming Your Temperament, Tim LaHaye, Inspirational Press

Raising Responsible Kids, Jay Kesler, Wolgemuth & Hyatt

How to Raise Your Kids to Stand on Their Own Two Feet, Jim Sanderson, Congdon & Weed

Building Stronger Families, Royce Money, Victor Press

Building Your Mate's Self Esteem, Dennis & Barbara Rainey, Here's Life Publishing

Love Life, Ed Wheat, Zondervan

The Birth Order Book, Kevin Leman, Fleming H. Revell Company

Caring Enough to Not Forgive, David Augsburger, Regal

Caring Enough to Forgive, David Augsburger, Regal

For Better or For Best, Gary Smalley, Zondervan

Solution Focused Marriage, The Meadors, Life Focus Publishing

Secrets of Staying in Love, Ruth Stafford Peale, Thomas Nelson Publishing

Men: Some Assembly Required, Chuck Snyder, Tyndale House Publishing

The Language of Love, Gary Smalley/John Trent, Focus on the Family

If Only He Knew, Gary Smalley, Zondervan

Talking Together About Love and Sexuality, Mildred Tengbom, Bethany House

Celebration in the Bedroom, Charlie & Martha Shedd, Word Books

Love Is a Choice, Hemfelt, Minirith & Meier, Thomas Nelson

Marking Your Children for God, Anne Gimenez, Creation House

What Every Woman Should Know about a Man, James L. Johnson, Zondervan

Intended for Pleasure, Ed & Gaye Wheat, Fleming H. Revell

An Ounce of Prevention, Gary Richmond, Christian Life Resources

Spirit Controlled Temperament, Tim LaHaye, Tyndale House

Creative Conversation Starters for Couples, Robert & Pamela Crosby, Focus on the Family

The Financial Planning Workbook, Larry Burkett, Moody Press

Growing Kids God's Way, Gary & Anne Marie Ezzo, Growing Families International

Boundaries, Cloud & Townsend, Zondervan

Dare to Discipline, James Dobson, Focus on the Family

Men Mentoring Men, Daryl Donovan, CSS Publishing Company, Inc.

The Inheritance, Daryl Donovan, Mentoring Ministries, Inc.

The Act of Marriage, Tim & Beverly LaHaye, Zondervan